MICHAEL FARADAY

MICHAEL FARADAY

THE
ROADMAKER
SERIES

MICHAEL FARADAY

(1791-1867)

By

WILFRID L. RANDELL

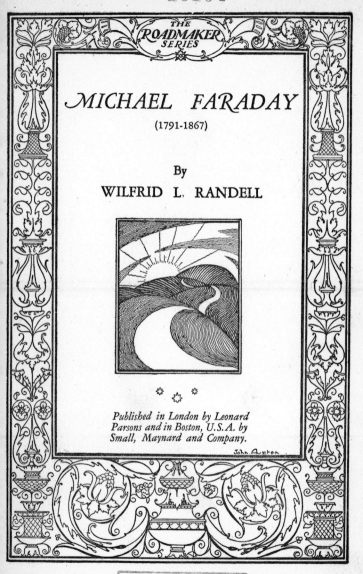

❖ ❖ ❖

*Published in London by Leonard
Parsons and in Boston, U.S.A. by
Small, Maynard and Company.*

John Arter

First Published 1924 by Leonard Parsons
Ltd., and Printed in Guernsey, C.I. by the
Guernsey Star and Gazette Company, Ltd.

FOREWORD

AUTHORITATIVE biographers of Michael Faraday have been, as a rule, scientists. In their selections from the available papers and correspondence they have disregarded, no doubt purposely, much material which to them seemed unimportant, and have gone too deeply into expositions of his scientific achievements for the taste of the reader unversed in electrical and chemical knowledge ; giving others a clearer picture of the scientist, but a less appealing picture of the man.

Of recent years several fresh documents have been added to the store accessible concerning Faraday. The generosity of Mr. Blaikley, who presented to the Institution of Electrical Engineers many most interesting collections of letters and records, and of Mr. A. Evelyn Barnard, nephew of Miss Jane Barnard, Faraday's niece, who gave the remarkable *Flower Book* to the Royal Institution and several items of Faraday's original

apparatus to the Science Museum at South
Kensington, cannot be too gratefully recognised. From this material we are able to
gain a better all-round view of the first
scientist of his century than has before been
possible, and to the Institution of Electrical
Engineers and the Royal Institution, their
librarians in particular, I wish to express my
thanks for courteous assistance in my inquiries ; to Mr. A. E. Barnard for his kindness and helpful conversation ; and to Sir
Henry Fielding Dickens, K.C., for his most
cordial consent to the publication of the
letters from Charles Dickens to Faraday here
printed.

The scientific aspect cannot, of course, be
omitted—it is the reason for Faraday's fame
as a pioneer ; but my immediate aim has
been to present the man himself, and in endeavouring to do this I have included many
quotations from letters and papers which,
while not of vital importance, serve to throw
some additional light upon his charming
personality.

To the original two-volume *Life* of Faraday by his friend Dr. Bence Jones, and to the

FOREWORD

smaller biographies by Professor Tyndall, Dr. Gladstone, and Professor Silvanus Thompson, all writers on Faraday must acknowledge indebtedness. These were men who knew him and loved him and, where necessary, I have taken freely from their invaluable work.

W.L.R.

London, 1924

CONTENTS

CHAPTER ONE

Why He is Famous

THERE is a sense in which every research worker, every inventor, even every patient amateur investigator, is a pioneer, since each by his labours adds to the sum of human knowledge. Yet those who merely extend the application of principles already accepted are less entitled to the term than those who actually discover a new principle ; and when experimental research is persevered in for years by one man, who succeeds at last in discovering proof of a theory long suspected to be true, or in establishing a law hitherto unconfirmed, the application of which to industry and commerce affects the whole world for generations to come, that man has well earned the honoured name of pioneer—of one who prepares the way and makes straight the path.

Such a man was Michael Faraday, and it detracts nothing from his fame to say that

Michael Faraday

had he failed, or had he not existed, another
brain would in due time have traced a
sequence of thought similar to his, would
have made experiments and deductions lead-
ing to the same far-reaching results. That
is extremely likely ; we have evidence in
analogous matters—as when the position
of Neptune in the skies was fixed, before
the planet was ever recognisably seen, by
Adam of Cambridge and Leverrier of Paris,
each of whom, in 1846, independently calculated its place from the observed perturba-
tions of Uranus, until then considered to
be the outermost planet of our solar system.
Had they not lived, Neptune would in-
evitably have been found ; the fact remains
that they discovered it, just as the fact
remains that Faraday, while carrying on his
experiments in electro-magnetism, found, by
no accident, but as the result of a clear
purpose, that a momentary current of electricity flowed within a wire when a magnet
approached or receded from it. It was an
experiment which we can perform to-day in
five minutes, in our own homes ; and one
remarkable point about it is that several

famous investigators of the phenomena of electro-magnetism—Ampère, for one—must have been on the very edge of the same discovery. They knew that electricity could produce magnetism ; it was reserved for Faraday, with his ever-alert, analytic mind, to settle the question : " If electricity can produce magnetism, cannot magnetism produce electricity ? " It was an example of his perpetual habit of examining a problem from all sides, of " reasoning backwards " and anticipating the corollary or reverse of an experiment ; but to answer that question took him many years. The habit was formed early in life—one might say it was born in him—and lasted for the whole of his working career. " Every morning," wrote his friend A. de la Rive of his work at the Royal Institution, " Faraday went into his laboratory as the man of business goes to his office, and then tried by experiment the truth of the ideas which he had conceived overnight." Continually we get these vivid glimpses of the indefatigable man of science, never satisfied unless he was either evolving or proving a theory. " The very last time I saw him

13

at work at the Royal Institution," Lord Kelvin said, " was in an underground cellar, which he had chosen for freedom from disturbance, and he was arranging experiments to test the time of propagation of magnetic force from an electro-magnet through a distance of many yards of air to a fine steel needle polished to reflect light ; but no result came from those experiments. About the same time, or soon after, certainly not long before the end of his working time, he was engaged (I believe at the Shot Tower, near Waterloo Bridge, on the Surrey side) in efforts to discover relations between gravity and magnetism, which also led to no result."

His mode of attacking any problem was intuitive rather than logical, though when on the track of a solution his reasoning, proceeding by process of elimination, of trial and error, was sound and logical enough. As William James observed acutely : " Some thoughts act almost like mechanical centres of crystallisation ; facts cluster of themselves about them." We cannot here go deeply into Faraday's theories, a full discussion of which would lead us into thickets of formulæ and byways of mathematics unsuitable for a book which is intended to describe the man and to indicate the principal lines of his achievement ; but it is within our province to give the opinions of his confrères on his manner of working out his thoughts. Helmholtz, in his Faraday Lecture of 1881, said : " It is in the highest degree astonishing to see what a large number of general theorems, the methodical deduction of which requires the highest powers of mathematical analysis, he found by a kind of intuition, with the security of instinct, without the help of a single mathematical formula." He repeats this, evidently impressed by such a gift : " With a quite wonderful sagacity and intellectual precision, Faraday performed in his brain the work of a great mathematician without using a single mathematical formula. . . ." " The fundamental conceptions by which Faraday was led to these much admired discoveries have not received an equal amount of consideration. They were very divergent from the trodden path of scientific theory, and appeared rather

15

startling to his contemporaries. His principal aim was to express in his new conceptions only facts, with the least possible use of hypothetical substances and forces. This was really an advance in general scientific method, destined to purify science from the last remnants of metaphysics. Faraday was not the first, and not the only man, who had worked in this direction, but perhaps nobody else at his time did it so radically."

Faraday admitted that he was no lover of mathematics, and pleaded almost pathetically in a letter to Clerk Maxwell in 1857, for some easier mode of expressing scientific ideas. "There is one thing I would be glad to ask you," he wrote. "When a mathematician engaged in investigating physical actions and results has arrived at his own conclusions, may they not be expressed in common language as fully, clearly, and definitely as in mathematical formulæ? If so, would it not be a great boon to such as we to express them so—translating them out of their hieroglyphics that we also might work upon them by experiment?" Always, we see, his mind returns to his one love—experimental work. Not for him the mathematician's joy of watching, on paper, the theories begin to fit, the symbols to range themselves in some sort of interpretative order and significant beauty ; his pleasure, just as keen, he found in watching the swing of a needle in response to some electrical or magnetic impulse, in a position or situation hitherto untried, or in examining, in every conceivable light, the behaviour of electricity.

Although it is by his discovery of the active relationship between magnetism and electricity, in the sense that electricity can be derived from magnetism, that Faraday most powerfully influences the modern world, it must not be forgotten that he broke new ground in the domain of chemistry. He attracted attention in 1820 by an account of his discovery of the chloride of carbon. His first published work was a treatise on *Chemical Manipulation*, which appeared in 1827. In this year also he delivered his first annual lecture on chemistry and physics at the Royal Institution. He spent much

time, and conducted a long series of experiments, upon the perfecting of glass as used
in optical instruments, and in 1829 read
the Bakerian Lecture before the Royal
Society, taking as his subject " The Manufacture of Glass for Optical Purposes." In
the year 1833, when Mr. Fuller founded at
the Royal Institution the Chair of Chemistry
called after his name, he nominated Faraday
as the first Professor. Later on, the spheres
of chemistry and magnetism intersect when
he discovered that oxygen was affected by
magnetism, and perceived the magnetic relation of gases and flames. He succeeded
in liquefying several gases ; he studied and
did practical work upon the alloys of steel.
Beneath all this, however, he carried on a
steady, persistent investigation, either by
actual experiment or in thought, of the
phenomena of electricity and of magnetism,
and it is for the final results of this that he
is chiefly known to-day. " It is only when
the right player comes, and the right cards
are judiciously dealt to him by fortune, that
the great successes can be accomplished,"
wrote Leslie Stephen, who knew more about

the art of biography than most people.   The rule has an impressive exception in Michael Faraday, who compelled fortune to come to him, as we shall see.

CHAPTER TWO

Shop to Laboratory

IT used to be the mode, in biography, to spring desperately at one's subject with a statement that he, or she, was born in a certain year—the date being given ; appending an equally unadorned announcement of the village, or town, and the county, thus honoured, with some information of the " poor but honest " type on parents and progenitors. If we begin, conventionally, with the date of Michael Faraday's birth, and continue, less conventionally, with that of his death, it is for a definite and practical reason, for September 22, 1791, seems to " place " him in a period that may fairly be termed remote, while August 28, 1867, seems to bring him notably near to us—so near, in fact, as to be included by the memory of many still living.

The years thus bridged formed a remarkably interesting period ; how interesting and significant we may linger to consider later on ; for within them lived and worked a host of men who consciously or unconsciously had much to do with the progress in art, in literature, in science, which has resulted in our present degree of civilisation and certainty—as far as we may be certain while the end of knowledge is not yet perceived.

Faraday was thoroughly English. He was as striking an example of the mystery of genius as Turner, whose father was a hairdresser of Maiden Lane ; for his father, a Yorkshireman, was a blacksmith, and remained a blacksmith ; his brother Robert, born to the blacksmithing, ended as a gasfitter ; and his mother, who lived till 1838, had nothing but a rudimentary education, and could not enter at all into the pursuits of her brilliant son. She was, however, very proud of him. James Faraday was born on May 8, 1761 ; married in 1788 Margaret Hastwell, a farmer's daughter, and soon afterward came from the heart of country England to a spot which is now engulfed in the maze of South London—Newington, Surrey, where Michael was born. When the boy was five years old, a move was made to Jacob's Well Mews, Charles Street, Manchester square, where the family had rooms over a coach-house—an unpromising stage-setting, we may well think, for the opening act of a great scientist's career. Brought up amid the unfragrant litter of the Mews, in company the reverse of refined, and with an education which barely comprised the elements of reading, writing, and arithmetic, there seemed small enough prospect of immortality for the blacksmith's son who, about the year 1800, could have been seen on fine days playing marbles with other little boys in the roadways near Manchester Square. Ordinary boys, none more distinguished, then, than his fellows ; but Time lifted the curtain, and in after years, when the name of Michael Faraday added lustre to the rolls of all the scientific bodies of Europe, its owner used sometimes to point out, with a smile, the scene of these juvenile games, modest, as ever, in his world-wide success. To continue for a moment our metaphor, the second act of the play showed no appreciable improvement, for at ten years old, with school-days behind him, Michael took his first salaried post at the bookseller's and stationer's shop of Mr. Riebau, in Blandford Street, close to his home—as errand boy. Here he used to carry round the newspapers to his master's customers very early in the morning —Sundays not excepted—and call for them again later, " lending out " the daily papers for a small charge being then a general practice.

His parents were so poor that at one time —in 1801—it is said that they were glad to receive parish relief, Michael's share of the food being one loaf of bread a week. This statement appeared in Faraday's biography, written by his friend, Dr. Henry Bence Jones, M.D., M.A., F.R.S., F.R.C.P., D.C.L., Secretary of the Royal Institution, two volumes to which any subsequent writer on Faraday must give ample and grateful acknowledgments ; but he appears to have been misinformed on this point, for it was contradicted by Mr. George Barnard, Faraday's brother-in-law, in a letter to the *Times* of January 3, 1870. " It is quite a mistake," he wrote, " and never occurred, and his friends are anxious that it should be corrected." Faraday told him that at the beginning of the week his mother used to give him a quartern loaf for himself, that he " might have the management of it entirely "; he immediately marked it out carefully into fourteen portions, one of which he " managed " each morning and evening. Evidently the family at this period lived within the penumbra, if not in the actual shadow, of poverty.

There seemed nothing to do but to pursue this modest start in business—unpropitious, we may deem it, but doubtless there were pleasant parental visions of the lad earning a decent wage as a book-binder, perhaps some day even possessing a shop of his own ; for on completing a year of running errands, with its accompaniments of shop-sweeping and window-cleaning, Michael was apprenticed to the trade at the same establishment, his indentures being dated October 7, 1805. Beneath the surface, however, his mind was awakening, betraying the nature of activities unexpected and unaccountable, veering towards the channels which were to guide it, and were eventually to be widened by its efforts during the whole course of his life. Some little help came at this time from M. Masquerier, a French artist lodging with Riebau, who lent him books and taught him the elements of drawing, and whose friendship was still valued in after years.

Many volumes bearing upon scientific subjects naturally passed through his hands ; he bound them as a duty, read them as a joy. Ned Magrath, secretary to the Athenæum, has recorded that one day, entering Riebau's shop, he saw one of the employees absorbed in the study of a book—reading it when he ought to have been binding it. He spoke to this young man, and found that the attraction was a volume of the old *Encyclopædia Britannica*, open at the article on " Electricity " ; as the two conversed, he was astonished to discover that he was speaking with " a self-taught chemist of no slender pretensions." This was Michael Faraday, the bookbinder's apprentice. The subjects of science in general, electricity and chemistry in particular, fascinated him ; in his 'teens he kept notebooks in which he entered the names of various books and articles which he had read and which had specially interested him, also copied extracts from all kinds of sources. Indexed and paged carefully, these books form a scientific medley which any boy of a similar turn of mind would thoroughly enjoy reading to-day. The subjects vary from Fairy Rings to Flies, from Sympathetic Inks to the copy of a cutting which tells how " Mr. B. Cook, of Birmingham," had lighted his workshops by home-made coal gas. The index shows, however, that Electricity has the most frequent place. I have copied the title-page of the first of these notebooks, and only wish I could give a reproduction of Faraday's beautiful-executed ornamental capitals and delicate penmanship :

THE PHILOSOPHICAL MISCELLANY.

being

A collection of Notices, Ocurrances, Events, &c. relating to the Arts & Sciences; collected from the Public Papers, Reviews, Magazines and other miscellaneous works.

Intended to promote both Amusement and Instruction and also to coroborate or invalidate those theories which are continually starting into the world of science.

Collected by M. Faraday, 1809–10

Faraday took the pains to illustrate the items which needed it by very competent pen and ink sketches. His spelling, however, was occasionally weak.

Additional evidence upon the bent of his mind comes in a letter written to his friend Abbott just before the finish of his apprenticeship :

" There are problems, the solution of which will be difficult to obtain, but the science of electricity will not be complete without them ; and a philosopher will aim at perfection, though he may not hit it— difficulties will not retard him, but only cause a proportionate exertion of his mental faculties."

Serious, stilted words from a youth of just 21 years of age ! Yet we shall see that Faraday must not be judged by the solemn tone of many of his letters. Of his first recorded experiment, in fact, he wrote to the same friend in a jovial strain, and as it bears both on chemistry and electricity the letter finds a place here. He was beginning to take a definite interest, which could not be satisfied by mere reading, in the wonders of electricity ; moved to actual experiment, he employed his leisure in the construction of an " electrical machine " and other workable apparatus. He tells Abbott, who was about his own age, of the astonishing results of an attempt to make and use a voltaic pile :—

" I, Sir, I my own self, cut out seven discs of the size of halfpennies each ! I, Sir, covered them with seven halfpence, and I interposed between seven, or rather six, pieces of paper soaked in a solution of muriate of soda ! But laugh no longer, dear A. ; rather wonder at the effects this trivial power produced. It was sufficient to produce the decomposition of sulphate of magnesia—an effect which extremely surprised me ; for I did not, could not, have any idea that the agent was competent to the purpose."

Much was to happen between the date of this letter, 1812, and the time when its

writer's name was to be honoured throughout
the world for electrical discoveries ; but it
was obvious that sooner or later opportunity
would smile on such an eager neophyte.
The great opportunity of his life came when
he made the acquaintance of Sir Humphry
Davy, and the manner in which that acquaintance arose throws an interesting light on the
perseverance so characteristic of Faraday.
He made his own opportunity—insisted on
having his chance, we might say ; led up to
it through his years of apprentice-work. He
read all the scientific books he could find,
borrow, or buy—though to buy a book was a
rare treat. One of these, we know, was Mrs.
Marcet's *Conversations on Chemistry*—a title
which irresistibly reminds us of *Mrs. Mark-
ham's England* and *Mangnall's Questions*.
This lady, her full and flowing name Jane
Haldimand Marcet, was the wife of Alex-
andre Marcet, a clever Swiss physician and
chemist who had made London his home.
Her book, written in English, passed through
many editions, and later on, in 1816, she
produced a treatise in a still sterner vein,
Conversations in Political Economy, which

Macaulay admired. " Every girl," said the austere historian, " who has read Mrs. Marcet's dialogues on political economy could teach Montague or Walpole many lessons on finance." The lady thus eulogised lived until 1858, and perhaps her best title to remembrance—one can hardly call it fame—is that she bore her part in the education of young Faraday. In after years she consulted him upon one of his own discoveries, and, to his great pleasure, he came to know her personally.

He made as many experiments in chemistry as he could afford on the weekly pocket-money that formed his wage ; he constructed several scientific models, his " electrical machine " being still preserved at the Royal Institution. With his mind thus settling into its inevitable direction, he happened to notice, when walking one day near Fleet Street, a bill announcing some evening lectures on natural philosophy by a Mr. Tatum, at 53 Dorset Court (now Dorset Street), Salisbury Square. Here was a chance of another refreshing draught for his thirsty mind ; but the price of admission was a

shilling. How overcome this difficulty ?
His brother Robert, three years his senior,
who carried on his father's trade of blacksmith and later on rose on the tide of progress
to become a gas-fitter, helped him—all
honour to Robert !—and between February,
1810, and September, 1811, he attended
about a dozen of these lectures, making
among the audience a friend or two who lent
him books on chemistry.[1] One of these
friends was Benjamin Abbott, a clerk in the
city, whom we have already mentioned.

Gradually, surely, he was preparing himself for the future ; yet that future, as far
as he could see, was to be spent in binding
books, for on October 8, 1812, after eight
years with Mr. Riebau, he went as journeyman bookbinder to M. de la Roche, a French
emigrant then in London. This man's
temperament, however, proved antipathetic
to that of Faraday, and after a short time he
left. It is perfectly clear that business and
its methods did not appeal to him at all.

[1] His father died in 1810, at 18, Weymouth Street,
Portland Place, where the family had moved some time
previously.

31

" The desire to be engaged in scientific occupation, even though of the lowest kind," he wrote afterward, " induced me, whilst an apprentice, to write, in my ignorance of the world and simplicity of my mind, to Sir Joseph Banks, then President of the Royal Society. Naturally enough, ' no answer ' was the reply left with the porter." But the event which was to open the gates for him was now near at hand.

A customer of his master named Dance, who was a member of the Royal Institution, became interested in this studious youth, seemed to perceive in him the square peg in the round hole, and took him to hear a course of four lectures on chemistry delivered at the Institution by Sir Humphry Davy. This was in 1812 ; and the lectures took place on February 29, March 14, April 8 and April 10. Davy, then thirty-four years of age and recently knighted, had sprung into fame twelve years before by the publica- tion of his *Chemical and Philosophical Re- searches*, which had gained for him the Royal Institution professorship of chemistry at the early age of twenty-two. We can picture the excitement with which Michael Faraday listened to the discourses of a man who to him must have appeared a hero ; one writer paints him as " perched, pen in hand, and his eyes starting out of his head, just over the clock opposite the chair." Yet, with all his hero-worship, the youngster had something of the quality of glorified " cheek " ; for, after having taken full notes of these lectures, he elaborated them, copied them out, bound them, and, still encouraged by Mr. Dance, actually sent them in December, 1812, to Sir Humphry, with a letter expressing his longing to leave business and asking the great scientist's help in obtaining some more congenial and more scientific occupation. This book, as fresh to-day as it was a century and more ago, rests, a treasure upon which no money value could be set, in the archives of the Royal Institution. The biographers of Faraday have passed it over with too casual a mention. It is a volume to delight any connoisseur. Its title-page, and the sub-titles of the different lectures, exquis-itely pen-printed in decorative lettering, and its neat, regular script, give one that subtle

33   c

pleasure which is specially inspired by the examination of a work of delicate art or craft. No wonder Sir Humphry, receiving such a compliment, felt compelled to respond; it was the finest credential any ambitious youth could have presented.

Many years after, Faraday told the story in a letter to Dr. Paris, Davy's biographer. " My desire to escape from trade," he said, " which I thought vicious and selfish, and to enter into the service of Science, which I imagined made its pursuers amiable and liberal, induced me at last to take the bold and simple step of writing to Sir H. Davy, expressing my wishes, and a hope that if an opportunity came in his way he would favour my views; at the same time, I sent the notes I had taken of his lectures." It speaks well for the eminent chemist that he recognised in his youthful correspondent some quality that would pay for training—although he was at first puzzled, and possibly amused. One of Faraday's notes ran thus : " Mr. Davy now proceeded to comment and make observations on the former theory of chlorine gas. Here I was unable to follow him " ;

at which one imagines the professor of chemistry chuckling quietly—little knowing that in a few years this naïve young binder of books would be as great a chemist as himself, and a greater lecturer.

The incident was the first contact of two minds which together have influenced the progress of chemical and electrical knowledge to an extent impossible to estimate. Davy realised that here was a youth who could not be ignored, so eagerly did he knock at the door that gave promise of liberation ; but for the moment Faraday was a problem. " What can I do with him ? " he asked Mr. Pepys, one of the managers of the Royal Institution, in humorous perplexity. " Do ? " said Pepys. " Put him to wash bottles ! You'll soon see what he's fit for." Possibly the letter chanced to come precisely at the right moment, for the laboratory of the Institution was wretchedly looked after, much to Sir Humphry's dissatisfaction. His notes in the *Journal* show this very clearly. " Objects much wanted in the laboratory of the Royal Institution : cleanliness, neatness, and regularity," he wrote.

" The laboratory must be cleaned every morning when operations are going on before 10 o'clock. It is the business of W. Payne to do this. . . . There must be in the laboratory pen, ink, paper, and wafers, and these must not be kept in the slovenly manner in which they are usually kept. I am now writing with a pen and ink such as was never used in any other place." All the instruments in the glass cases were to be cleaned and dusted at least once a month, and there were many other duties which W. Payne evidently did not fancy, even though they provided an opportunity for frequently rubbing shoulders with some of the greatest scientists and philosophers of the period and for daily work in one of the most famous laboratories of the world. It was a place where anyone with a taste for chemistry and for practical experiment would be blissfully happy in his task of polishing the beloved instruments, dusting the tables and books ; where one might perceive the glamour that " makes drudgery divine " ; might feel the invisible world of nature's mysteries towards which these patient, brilliant investigators

were reaching out, just as their successors
are doing to-day.

> " Who sweeps a room as for thy laws
> Makes that and the action fine."

So sang benignant George Herbert ; and
that was exactly Faraday's spirit when he
sent his letter. The consequence of his
temerity was that Davy, favourably impressed, replied kindly, and through his
efforts the blacksmith's son, the journeyman
bookbinder, stepped clear from trade to
science, from one career to another, at a
single stride. On Christmas Eve, 1812,
Faraday must have had one of the greatest
thrills of his life. The letter he received
from Sir Humphry we can emphasise, if we
will, by our knowledge of the art of modern
headlines. " World-famous Scientist Writes
to Unknown Workman " ; " Gratifying
Response of Our New Knight of Science to
An Appeal for Help " ; sensations best
translated, perhaps, by some such phrases,
must have sent a glow through the young
bookbinder on that memorable day. Sir

Humphry explained that he was compelled to leave town for a while, but would see Faraday at the end of January. " It would gratify me," he wrote, " to be of any service to you. I wish it may be in my power."

The interview, hoped for, possibly feared, took place ; and proved something in the nature of a dash of cold water ; for Sir Humphry advised Faraday to stick to his trade ; not only so, but promised to be his patron—to let him have the bookbinding work of the Royal Institution, as well as his own private custom and that of his friends, if possible. A less pertinacious youth, with a good craft at his finger-ends, might have given up the quest at this, and reckoned himself fortunate in having secured the interest of an influential personage ; we do not feel sure, even now, what Faraday thought about this business-like advice. For all we know he might have begun to contemplate a future in which he played the part of a master shopman, expounding the problems of bindery to other blacksmiths' sons, making out invoices, conning the price of fancy leathers. But one night, at the home in

38

Weymouth Street, just as he was getting ready for bed, he was startled by loud knockings at the front door ; startled still more, on looking from his window, to see a carriage and a footman waiting. The footman left a note for him—from Sir Humphry Davy, asking him to call at the Royal Institution on the next morning. And back, with all its brightness, came the vision.

At this second conversation Sir Humphry referred to the previous interview, and inquired if Faraday was still in the same mind. If so, he intimated, the post of assistant in the laboratory of the Royal Institution was vacant, from which he had on the previous day " ejected its former occupant "—the W. Payne mentioned previously—for striking the instrument-maker in a quarrel.

The answer was certain. At twenty-one Faraday was appointed assistant to the laboratory of the Royal Institution. Tremendous, incredible promotion ! In the minutes of a Managers' Meeting dated March 1, 1813, the event is placed on record :

" Sir Humphry Davy has the honour to inform the Managers that he has found a person who is desirous to occupy the situation in the Institution lately filled by William Payne. His name is Michael Faraday. He is a youth of 22 years of age. As far as Sir Humphry Davy has been able to observe or ascertain, he appears well fitted for the situation. His habits seem good, his disposition active and cheerful, and his manner intelligent. He is willing to engage himself on the same terms as those given to Mr. Payne at the time of quitting the Institution.

" Resolved : That Michael Faraday be engaged to fill the situation lately occupied by Mr. Payne on the same terms."

The " terms " were twenty-five shillings a week. Faraday took up his residence in two rooms at the top of the house on the date of this historic " Resolution " ; and thus began an association with the celebrated building in Albemarle Street, Piccadilly, which was to last without a break for his whole lifetime. And though Mr. Dance, who befriended the bookbinder's young man, knew not how well he was building, and has vanished in obscurity, we may spare him a kindly thought for the kindly acts which were to lead to so wondrous a progress.

CHAPTER THREE

The Young Scientist

IT is natural, when striving to paint a portrait of a famous man, that one should look for high lights and dark shadows, for splashes of colour, for "effects," since a mere conjunction of facts and dates gives us no portrait at all, but a featureless shape. In endeavouring to convey some idea of Faraday, however, particularly as a young man, difficulties are at once encountered ; the patient student finds himself almost wishing that this model youth might occasionally betray himself as of like passions to ourselves. He was, we might say, so excessively moral. We long for a burst of temper, a little "language," for some hint of a flirtation, for a trace of the animal spirits which used to expend themselves in wrenching off door-knockers, and, by the time we have read a few of his letters to his good friend Abbott, for even the ghost of a peccadillo, the slightest sign of a fall from grace, to

relieve the even terror of his way. Our taste
has perhaps been vitiated by an age which
prefers to placard in fierce publicity the
wickedness and sadness of the world and to
leave the happiness and often the truth un-
recorded ; yet, admitting this, we find
Faraday's early correspondence a trifle de-
pressing.

The interchanges of thought and experi-
ence with Abbott began on July 12, 1812,
three months before the end of Faraday's
apprenticeship, and the first eight letters
come within that period, while he was still
working for Mr. Riebau in Blandford Street.
" They possess an interest," says Dr. Bence
Jones, " almost beyond any other letters
which Faraday afterwards wrote "—in which
statement we feel an enthusiasm not easily
shared. " It is difficult to believe," he goes
on, " that they were written by one who had
been a newspaper boy and who was still a
bookbinder's apprentice, not yet twenty-one
years of age, and whose only education had
been the rudiments of reading, writing, and
arithmetic. Had they been written by a
highly-educated gentleman, they would have

been remarkable for the energy, correctness, and fluency of their style, and for the courtesy kindness, candour, deference, and even humility, of the thoughts they contain." And that last sentence expresses precisely the reason for our complaint ; they are courteous, kind, respectful, and many other things—and dull. Only here and there does the writer show a certain liveliness—as when in his first letter to Abbott he effervesces in a paragraph which I have already quoted relating to his home-made voltaic pile. That letter covers seven pages of the *Life* by Dr. Bence Jones.

It is worth while to look at one or two of these letters, merely to note their prevalent tone. Here is a part of one written to Abbott on October 11, 1812, three days after Faraday joined De la Roche :

" As for the change you suppose to have taken place in respect to my situation and affairs, I have to thank my late master that it is but little. Of liberty and time I have, if possible, less than before, though I hope my circumspection has not at the same time decreased. I am well aware of the irrepar-

43

able evils that an abuse of those blessings will give rise to. . . .   I cannot help but be pleased with the earnest manner in which you enforce the necessity of precaution in respect of new acquaintances.   I have long been conscious of it, and it is that conscious-ness which limits my friends to the very small number that comprises them."

And then he writes this astounding sentence : " I feel no hesitation in saying that I scrutinised you long and closely before I satisfied the doubts in my breast, but I now trust they are all allayed."   And Abbott apparently never replied : " You did, did you !   Well, I'm hanged ! "

He proceeds to give his ideas on the meaning of " true friendship and eligible companions " :

" I would define a friend, a true friend, to be ' one who will serve his companion next to his God ' ; nor will I admit that an im-moral person can fill completely the char-acter of a true friend,"

and so on, for sentence after sentence. These two boys of twenty-one were writing the most ponderous stuff to one another in the best " Friendship's Garland " mode, intent as any disciple of modern mental culture on mutual improvement. They didn't write letters ; they indited epistles. " I trust," says Faraday, in a letter dated April 9, 1813, " that not only mine, but your intentions also in writing are for the improvement not only of yourself but of me." We are impelled to give thanks that by the side of this picture we can set another one of Faraday, more than forty years later, explaining the principles of magnetism to an audience at the Royal Institution, when " he threw a coalscuttle full of coals, a poker, and a pair of tongs at the great magnet, and they stuck there ; the theatre echoed with shouts of laughter."

So fixed were these young men on propelling one another along the path of wisdom that they met continually for the exchange of ideas. " During this spring," Faraday writes, " Magrath and I established the mutual-improvement plan, and met at my rooms up in the attics of the Royal Institution, or at Wood Street at his warehouse. It consisted perhaps of half a dozen persons, chiefly from the City Philosophical Society, who met of an evening to read together, and to criticise, correct, and improve each other's pronunciation and construction of language." This " City Philosophical Society " was founded in 1808, probably by Mr. Tatum of Dorset Court, and its members, numbering thirty or forty, met at his house every Wednesday evening "for mutual instruction." Soon after Faraday had received his appointment at the laboratory of the Royal Institution and returned from his trip abroad he lectured to this little company of enthusiasts on chemistry ; but before we take up this part of his life some brief account must be given of his travels with Sir Humphry Davy, for the Continental journey, with its constant experiments and its opportunities for meeting well-known scientists, meant a great deal in the education and technical training of the boy who was to become the first scientist of his century.

46

CHAPTER FOUR

The Continental Tour

O NE of Michael Faraday's first duties,
on becoming a member of the staff
of the Royal Institution, pleased him greatly.
He accompanied Sir Humphry Davy on a
journey to the Continent in 1813, acting as
secretary, amanuensis, and for a part of the
time—somewhat to his disgust—as valet.
He got on very well with the famous Cornish-
man, but, he writes, " Lady Davy is of
another humour. She likes to show her
authority, and at first I found her extremely
earnest in mortifying me."

His work at the Royal Institution had
begun early in March, 1813 ; the excursion
abroad lasted from October of that year until
April, 1815. The party sailed from Ply-
mouth, and Faraday's journal, with his
letters home, presents an interesting picture,
or series of pictures, of foreign travel in
those days. He kept this record, he says,
" not to instruct or inform "—strange words

47

from so persistent an advocate of " improvement " on every possible occasion—" or
to convey even an imperfect idea of what it
speaks ; its sole use is to recall to my mind
at some future time the things I see now, and
the most effectual way to do that will be, I
conceive, to write down be they good or bad
or however imperfect my present Impres-
sions." So runs, in his neat handwriting,
the opening sentence on a separate flyleaf of
the Journal.

Landing at Morlaix in Brittany, Paris was
reached on the 29th, and he notes the irrita-
tion he felt at his ignorance of the language ;
also, " the people are enemies, and they are
vain." [1] Only a registered inhabitant of
the city was permitted to go about without a
passport, and from Faraday's account of his
visit to the Prefecture of Police to obtain
one we gain a hint of his appearance at the
age of twenty-two : " a round chin, a brown
beard, a large mouth, a great nose." Incidents recorded of the stay in Paris are not

---

[1] On the last day of 1813 the Allied forces crossed the
Rhine, and " a third of France passed, without opposition,
into their hands."—J.R. Green.

much above the trivial, but one morning Ampère called to show Sir Humphry a new substance (iodine) discovered by M. Courtois, saltpetre manufacturer, upon which several experiments were carried out ; on another day Sir Humphry and Faraday went to hear Gay-Lussac [1] lecture at l'Ecole Polytechnique, Faraday missing most of it owing to the slightness of his knowledge of French ; and on December 18, when the Emperor Napoleon visited the Senate in full state, he saw " the show " from the Tuilleries Gardens. The French capital does not appeal to him very strongly. " I am quite out of patience with the infamous exorbitance of these Parisians," he writes ; " they seem to have neither sense of honesty nor shame in their dealings." And, naturally, to a Puritan, " a tasteless heretic " as he calls himself, the churches were " theatrical " ; he found it " impossible to attach a serious or important feeling to what was going on." The strain

[1] Famous for his balloon ascents while investigating the expansion of gases. Professor of Chemistry at L'Ecole Polytechnique in 1816, and afterwards a member of the Chamber of Deputies and a peer of France.

of narrowness betrayed here belonged to
Faraday's youth ; in his later life it appeared
very rarely. The real man, in these years,
was in process of formation ; and intolerance
was never a word to be justly applied to him.

Leaving Paris on December 29, the party
travelled via Nemours, Moulins, Mont-
pellier, and Aix to Nice, and thence to Genoa,
where a visit to the opera is described, and
some experiments were made on the gym-
notus or " torpedo "—the electrical eel.
March, 1814, found them at Florence.
" Here was much to excite interest," writes
the young scientist ; but not a single word is
said about the treasures of art within a hand's
reach—it was Galileo's first telescope, " a
simple tube of wood and paper about $3\frac{1}{2}$
feet long, with a lens at each end," which
excited him. He describes the electrical
apparatus at the Academy del Cimento, and,
at some length, " the grand experiment of
burning the diamond " with the great
burning-glass of the Duke of Tuscany. On
April 7 they arrived at Rome, and a post-
script to a letter to his mother dated April 14
gives us one of those human touches which

infuse life into the bare facts of history-books :

"There is no certain road open at present by which you can write to me, so that, much as I wish it, it must be deferred a little longer. We have heard this morning that Paris was taken by the Allied troops on March 31, and, as things are, we may soon hope for peace, but at present all things are uncertain. Englishmen are here respected almost to adoration, and I proudly own myself as belonging to that nation which holds so high a place in the scale of European Powers."

Rome awakens his sense of beauty by her antiquities and works of art, though natural scenes always roused his greater appreciation. "You know, Ben," he writes to Abbott, "my turn is not architectural, nor, though I can admire a beautiful picture, do I pretend to judge of it ; but certainly the things here would affect anyone." In the same letter he says : "There are many things in Paris calculated in an eminent degree to arrest the progress of the traveller, but these things consist in the works of man, and I would rather talk to you of the works of nature." At Rome experiments were made on the magnetisation of a needle by the rays of the sun. From Naples, which at that time was not a part of Italy, two ascents of Vesuvius are vividly described. On June 17 occurs the entry : " Saw M. Volta, an hale, elderly man, wearing the red ribbon, and very free in conversation." Volta had called to see Davy, and was then 69 years of age. " His conversation was not brilliant," says Davy ; " his gaze was dull, but still frank ; his manners were of a perfect simplicity." But he was a great figure, Count Volta.

A long stay was made in Geneva, and we can perceive that Faraday's education was progressing rapidly, as it was bound to do on such a journey, even had he been in commonplace company ; but with the constant presence of Sir Humphry, which he terms " a mine inexhaustible of knowledge and improvement," the frequent meetings with famous Continental scientists, and the almost incessant experiments, there was every chance for the attentive student and assistant. He writes however, the most tedious epistles to his friend, covering pages of print. Plati-

tude after platitude rolls from his pen—
Abbott was equally expert at it—and I quote
a few sentences merely to show how unjust
it would be to accept them as a true indication
of his mind.   This letter is dated " Geneva,
September 6, 1814 " :

" In passing through life, my dear friend,
everyone must expect to receive lessons both
in the school of prosperity and in that of ad-
versity ; and, taken in a general sense, these
schools do not only include riches and poverty,
but everything that may cause the happiness
and pleasure of man, and every feeling that
may give him pain. . . .   With respect to
myself, I have always perceived (when, after
a time, I saw things more clearly) that those
things which at first appeared as misfortune
or evils ultimately were actually benefits,
and productive of much good in the future
progress of things. . . .   I have observed
that, in the progress of things, circumstances
have so worked together, without my knowing how or in what way, that an end has
appeared which I would never have fancied,
and which circumstances ultimately showed
could never have been attained by any plans
of mine.   I have found also that those circumstances which I have earnestly wished

for, and which ultimately I have obtained, were productive of effects very different to those I had assigned to them, and were oftentimes more unsatisfactory than even a disappointment would have been. I have experienced, too, that pleasures are not the same when attained as when sought after ; and from these things I have concluded that we generally err in our opinions of happiness and misery. . . ."

Abbott enjoyed this uplifting stuff, asked for more, and could write, on occasion, reams of it himself. It suggests the stage curate, with dank hair and a black handbag ; but if a smile is permissible at these two young platitudinarians, laughter would be unfair, for hypocrisy was unknown to either of them. They were absolutely sincere, very good, and, at times, extraordinarily heavy-handed.

The same letter contains the first hint of dissatisfaction with his surroundings. " I find the prospect so different from what it first appeared to be," he says, " that I am certain, if I could have foreseen the things that have passed, I should never have left London " ; but his splendid opportunities of " improving " in the knowledge of chemistry and the sciences determine his decision to finish the tour. There is a suggestion of a momentary jealousy on the part of Sir Humphry when Professor de la Rive, a physician and chemist, invited them both to dinner, and Davy, it is said, refused to dine with his assistant ; de la Rive offering the retort courteous by expressing regret that he would have to give two dinners instead of one. Forty years later Faraday wrote to de la Rive's more distinguished son that his father was " the first who personally at Geneva, and afterwards by correspondence," encouraged him.

The journey continued to Vicenza, Padua, Munich, and Venice, a pleasing description of Venice occurring in one of Faraday's letters to his mother—those affectionate letters which he never failed to write when away from her. Back again at Rome in November, 1814, he sends another sheet or two of moral talk to the ever-absorbent Abbott. The Christmas carnival at Rome does not please him—its " frivolous spirit," he thinks, " debases the empire which once

stood like a Colossus over the whole world " ;
but the city once more fills him with awe and
respect.

His first letter to Abbott in 1815 tells the
secret of his growing discontent. He had
been engaged as assistant ; but Davy's valet
had failed to accompany the party, and
Faraday had to do a good many things which
he had not bargained for—to see after expenses, the servants, the table, and the
accommodation. Apparently, however, no
great trouble occurred ; " Sir Humphry
has no valet except myself," Faraday writes,
" but having been in an humbler situation,
and not being corrupted by high life, he
has very little occasion for a servant of that
kind, and 'tis the name more than the thing
that hurts." He would have little to com-
plain of, he says, if he were travelling with
Sir Humphry alone, or were Lady Davy
like him ; " but her temper makes it oftentimes go wrong with me, with herself, and
with Sir H." Quarrels occurred, " at each
of which I gained ground, and she lost it ;
for the frequency made me care nothing
about them, and weakened her authority,

and after each she behaved in a milder
manner." It is a surprise, in one letter, to
find him inclined to resume his former trade
of bookbinding ; this, however, must have
been the expression of a fleeting mood, for it
is quite evident from his recurring descrip-
tions of experimental work that his heart was
in the study of science.

One feels a sense of relief, after the lengthy
essays in mental deportment of which examples have been given, at a little picture of
Faraday joining " all Rome " and " all the
English besides " at a masked ball, attired
in a nightgown and nightcap, accompanied
by a lady whom he did not know but who
knew all his friends and acquaintances. We
breathe freely : Faraday was human. It
brings him more into line with our ideas of
what a normally healthy youth should be.
His sentences recounting this evening's
amusement might have been penned by
Pepys. " Between us," he concludes, " we
puzzled them mightily, and we both came
away well entertained." We long for this
unknown lady's opinion of her squire.

Sir Humphry's researches, while on this

journey, added considerably to chemical knowledge, particularly with regard to the nature of iodine and its combinations, and the action of chlorine with oxygen ; the whole record of the journey as given by Faraday abounds in references to these investigations. Towards the spring of 1815 it had been the intention to extend the tour through the near East and Turkey, but, for reasons that are not very clear, the turn for England was made in April, after a second visit to Naples and Vesuvius. To his mother Faraday writes on April 16 from Brussels :

" My Very Dear Mother,—It is with no small pleasure I write you my last letter from a foreign country, and I hope it will be with as much pleasure you will hear I am within three days of England. . . . At Ostend we embark, and at Deal we land on a spot of earth which I will never leave again. . . . Adieu till I see you, dearest Mother; and believe me ever your affectionate and dutiful son,

M. Faraday."

" 'Tis the shortest and (to me) the sweetest letter I ever wrote you."

This foreign tour, lasting eighteen months, said Professor Silvanus P. Thompson, addressing the Institution of Electrical Engineers in 1915, " was for Faraday what residence at a university is for many other men." It occurred at precisely the right point in his life, when his mind was pliant and receptive, and nothing, just then, could have been better for him.

CHAPTER FIVE

Science in 1791

A FIGURE without a background stands out too sharply, with uncorrected values and unqualified significance, to please our critical eyes ; like a silhouette, it has shape, but lacks the warmth of colour. We shall better estimate and appreciate Michael Faraday if we can retrieve from history " the tone of time," the tints and half-lights and weatherings which serve to modify the stark relief of the unaccompanied outline ; they will serve also to rest and focus our gaze, otherwise, perhaps, too strained upon a single object.

Human knowledge advances in waves. ' Great men appear in great ages," wrote Professor Henry Jones in a beautiful and memorable book,[1] " and they are the creatures of what they create. They come in ' the fulness of time,' their messengers sent before

[1] *Idealism as a Practical Creed.* By Professor Henry Jones, LL.D., D.Litt. (Maclehose, Glasgow).

their face, into a world which is waiting for them. They are the consequences of vast upheavals, products of the world's stress and strain, pushed upwards from beneath by the pressure of mute social forces which have been long mustering. For this reason great men come, not singly as a rule, but in groups, like highest peaks in a mountainous region. The greatest of them does not stand alone, nor does he rise abruptly from the level plain." Accepting these words as a generalisation which approaches truth, we look, therefore, for some evidence of it concerning our immediate theme ; and we look logically in the domain of science. What great men raised their torches, beaconed and beckoned the younger generations, in the years of Faraday's birth-century ? Our minds fix at once upon Franklin—clerk, printer, author, newspaper-owner, politician, diplomatist, tallow-chandler, President of the State of Pennsylvania, and, more to our point, ardent electrician. His biographer grows lyrical about him. " He subjected electricity to every test and every influence that the most fertile brain in the world could suggest.

He tried it upon magnets. He tried it in vacuo. He tried it upon the sick and upon the well ; upon animals and men. The electricity excited by friction, the electricity drawn from the clouds, the electricity generated in the cold and glittering winter nights, the electricity of the electric eel "—this spoils our lyric—" were all observed and compared. He became the acknowledged head of the electricians of the world." From 1747 to 1751 Franklin had been writing the results of his own investigations to his friend Collinson, in London, by whom they were read to the Royal Society—at first, as he says, " only to be ignored or laughed at." In 1749 came his " Opinions and Conjectures concerning the Properties and Effects of the Electrical Matter, and the means of preserving Buildings, Ships, etc., from Lightning, arising from Experiments and Observations made at Philadelphia, 1749." Note the modesty of the man as it escapes in his words : " Observations, Suppositions, Opinions, Conjectures ! " This paper seems to have broken the ice of convention at last ; it was translated into French, German, and Latin ;

it circulated almost as freely as a modern
specimen of " best seller," and caused a
tremendous sensation. The identity of
electricity and lightning ; the suggestion
that by pointed iron electricity might be
actually " drawn from a storm-cloud," and
buildings and ships protected from the
dreaded stroke—these were big ideas in
those days. I cannot resist giving here a
sentence by Dr. Priestley, who tells us that
at the close of the first summer of Franklin's
experiments, when the weather grew too
hot to continue them, he had a " party "
on the banks of the Schuykill River, " at
which spirits were first fired by a spark
sent from side to side through the river
without any other conductor than the water ;
a turkey was killed for their dinner by the
electrical shock and roasted by the electrical
jack, before a fire kindled by the electrified
bottle,[1] when the health of all the famous
electricians in England, Holland, France,
and Germany was drunk in electrified
bumpers under a discharge of guns from the
electrical battery." A merry party ; and

[1] The Leyden jar.

63

one imagines that an electrical ambulance would have been of some assistance after it was over.

On May 25, 1787, just four years before Faraday was born, Dr. Benjamin Franklin, in that historic scene in the State House of Philadelphia, then 81 years of age and the oldest member of the assembly, signed, with others, the Articles of the Constitution of the United States of America.

The century was a dark age of electricity regarded from our later point of vantage, in spite of all Franklin's honours, for in many countries the impiety of using lightning-rods was discussed, and this method of insuring houses against fire denounced as a presumptuous attempt to assume the rights of the Deity. Mr. Ebenezer Kinnersley, who for years lectured on electricity, actually announced at the opening of his discourses his intention of showing that the erection of lightning-rods was " not chargeable with presumption, nor inconsistent with any of the principles of natural or revealed religion." And in the very year of Faraday's birth a mob attacked and burned the house of

Dr. Joseph Priestley, F.R.S., at Birmingham; to which outrage Priestley replied in a letter so fine in its dignity that it is well worth reading :

July 19, 1791.

To the Inhabitants of the town of Birmingham.

MY LATE TOWNSMEN AND NEIGHBOURS,

You have destroyed the most truly valuable and useful apparatus of philosophical instruments that perhaps any individual, in this or any other country, was ever possessed of, in my use of which I annually spent large sums with no pecuniary view whatever, but only in the advancement of Science, for the benefit of my country and mankind. You have destroyed the Library corresponding to that apparatus, which no money can re-purchase, except in course of time. But what I feel far more, you have destroyed manuscripts which have been the result of the laborious study of many years, and which I shall never be able to recompose ; and this has been done to one who never did, or imagined, you any harm.

In this business we are the sheep and you

the wolves. We will preserve our character and hope you will change yours. At all events we return you blessings for curses, and hope that you shall soon return to that industry and those sober manners for which the inhabitants of Birmingham were formerly distinguished.

Yours faithfully,
J. PRIESTLEY.

The discoveries of Alessandro Volta were made in the century, and by 1791—our pivotal date—he had become famous, though his most celebrated achievement, the construction of the " electric pile," did not take place until 1800. The voltaic pile, or battery, as we should term it, consisted of a number of discs of tin and copper or silver, in pairs, each pair separated by some porous material kept moist by a saline or slightly acid infusion. With the aid of this invention, which provided for the first time quite a respectably strong continuous current of electricity, Volta carried out many interesting and extremely valuable experiments, and proved that the effects produced were identical with those which could be obtained from electrical machines (frictional), and that " galvanism " and electricity were really the same. He was first Professor of Physics in the University of Pavia—the Chair of Physics having been founded in 1779 ; and in 1791 our own Royal Society, which has never recognised national boundaries to knowledge, conferred upon him the distinction of the Copley Medal. The interdependence of scientists is interestingly shown when we remember that by means of the voltaic pile Sir Humphry Davy, when Secretary of the Royal Society in 1807, succeeded in isolating the metals potassium and sodium—the brilliant beginning of a series of chemical discoveries which were the foundation of his fame. Without the preliminary experiments of the Italian *savant*, Davy might never have risen to his position of world-wide celebrity, though sooner or later others would have accomplished his task and reaped the triumph. Volta died in 1827—the year in which Davy was compelled by ill-health to relinquish the Presidency of the Royal Society.

In 1799 young André Ampère was packing

his mind with mathematics at Lyons ;
not until 1820 did he establish the relationship between electricity and magnetism upon
which his fame is chiefly founded—and, considering his persistence in these investigations, it is astonishing that not even by
chance did he hit upon the reverse of his
magnetic experiments. That not even by
reason did he hit this mark is perhaps more
astonishing still.

Electricity, the new, mysterious force, we
thus see gradually exercising the minds of
the scientists of the age—Franklin in
America, Davy in England, Ampère in
France, Oersted in Denmark, Volta in Italy,
Ohm in Germany ; each with his little group
of followers extending some phase of the
fascinating theme. For those versed in
scientific history these names sufficiently
orientate the world which Faraday was to
disturb so effectively ; but those who read
this book with minds differently stored may
like to see it from another angle. It was a
world of the days before Keats had sung,
before Wordsworth, Shelley, Byron, Scott,
had enchanted their thousands ; when the

unperturbing rhythms of Pope and Cowper
and Crabbe were accepted as the fine flower
of poetry, hardly to be outbloomed ; when
Samuel Richardson and Henry Fielding
were apostles of the art of fiction, rivalled
only by the recent fame of Frances Burney.
In 1791 Scott was a youth of twenty, about
to be called to the bar ; fourteen years later
he was to rouse enthusiasm with his first
original work as a poet, " The Lay of the
Last Minstrel." Byron was three years old ;
Wordsworth just leaving Cambridge to
begin that tour through France and Switzerland, in the crisis of the French Revolution,
which was to sway his thoughts so stormily.
Blake was thirty-four, and had published his
Songs of Innocence two years before ; neither
Keats nor Shelley was born. Mrs. Siddons
was queen of the Drury Lane stage ; Gar-
rick had been dead twelve years. Notes
such as these seem to place Faraday, for our
present younger generation, in a remote past;
but this feeling, finding emphasis when we
add that Dr. Johnson had died only seven
years before, and that Swift, linking with
the seventeenth century, with William III.

and Queen Anne, had been dead only forty-six years, may lessen when we bridge the centuries by recollecting that many now living in 1924 can remember Michael Faraday.

Nelson, in 1791, was thirty-three and a captain in the Navy, already famous; Wellington, at the age of twenty-two, was Member of the Irish Parliament for the borough of Trim; William Pitt was Prime Minister of England. James Watt was fifty-five, George Stephenson a boy of ten; our industries had just begun to accept the domination of steam as a source of power. Our cities had nothing better in illumination than oil lamps; in transport, the horse was supreme, the mail-coach a glory of the road. Priestley, theologian, philosopher, and chemist, the discoverer of oxygen, whose meeting with Benjamin Franklin caused him to take up the study of electricity, was fifty-eight, and a Fellow of the Royal Society; Franklin had died, at a ripe old age, the previous year. Arago, astronomer and natural philosopher, was a child of five.

With this sketch of the times as a background, we can proceed with our picture of Michael Faraday, having focussed him as clearly as may be against the general features of the century's close.

CHAPTER SIX

Lecturer and Scientist

AS assistant in the laboratory of the Royal Institution and superintendent of the apparatus, Faraday took up his full duties a fortnight after his return from the Continent, his salary being thirty shillings a week. A prominent feature in his life at this time was the City Philosophical Society, at which he began to lecture in January, 1816, chiefly on chemistry. Electricity, as yet, is in the background, but it is not forgotten—he emphasises " the close connection which exists between the electric power and that of chemical affinity." Here and there the reader is pleased by a passage of dignity, and even of beauty. He gives his ideas on the qualification of a philosopher :

" The philosopher should be a man willing to listen to every suggestion, but determined to judge for himself. He should not be biased by appearances ; have no favourite hypothesis ; be of no school ; and in doctrine have no master. He should not be a respecter of persons, but of things. Truth should be his primary object. If to these qualities be added industry, he may indeed hope to walk within the veil of the temple of nature."

His notebook contains sundry doggerel verses on "Love," contemptuous as only ignorance can be—he had not yet thought seriously of love or marriage, therefore could glibly write of love as "the pest and plague of human life," and "the curse that often brings a wife." In spite of this youthful scorn, it brought him the wife who was his helpmate through his whole career, as we shall see. More interesting at the moment is a rhyming impression of the lecturer by a friend in the audience at one of his lectures ; quite in the cherished narrative tradition:

But hark ! A voice arises near the chair !
Its liquid sounds glide smoothly through the
      air ;
The listening Muse with rapture bends to
      view
The place of speaking, and the speaker too.
Neat was the youth in dress, in person plain ;

73

His eye read thus, *Philosopher in grain* ;
Of understanding clear, reflection deep ;
Expert to apprehend, and strong to keep.
His watchful mind no subject can elude,
Nor specious arts of sophists e'er delude ;
His powers, unshackled, range from pole to
    pole ;
His mind from error free, from guilt his soul.
Warmth in his heart, good humour in his face,
A friend to mirth, but foe to vile grimace ;
A temper candid, manners unassuming,
Always correct, yet always unpresuming.

This is indeed " the homespun thread of rhymes." One almost apologises for introducing even a part of such a " poem," but it is from such scraps that our impression of the young man has to be formed.

His first published paper appeared this year (1816) in the *Quarterly Journal of Science*, and he may be said to be fairly launched as a scientist. Contributions by him began to appear with some frequency— six were published in 1817. He visited a friend named Huxtable at South Molton, Devonshire, in that year, and had a lively time ; " I have been at sheep-shearing, merry-making, junketings, etc., and was never more merry," he wrote to his mother from Barnstaple. In notes for a lecture he mentions the safety lamp, referring to Davy's famous invention as the only one that has been found efficacious ; and these memoranda of his present a strange mixture of chemistry and morals. Next door to paragraphs upon the nature of pleasure and pain come observations on the action of electricity upon sulphur and red lead. And from a letter to Abbott dated January 20, 1817, the first sentence must be quoted as another salutary example of his style—with the qualifying note that it was not often so heavy :

" DEAR A.,—The irresistible propensity in the human breast to draw conclusions, before every circumstance has been examined, or even before possession has been obtained of the necessary data, is so general, that it passes unnoticed, although constantly active in ourselves, until some very flagrant instance in others draws the attention to the results of such irregular and improper proceedings, and points out the folly of immature judgments. . . ."

Towards the end of this year he increased his small income by coaching in mineralogy and chemistry, a pupil having been recommended to him by Sir Humphry Davy. With his practical work, however, the steady note of " improvement " still prolongs its undertone. Among his documents at the Royal Institution is a volume entitled—in his invariably beautiful penmanship—" A Class Book for the Reception of Mental Exercises, instituted July 1818," and bearing the names of M. Faraday, E. Deeble, E. Barnard, T. Deacon, and J. Corder. To this book each member of the " class " contributed original essays on the most diverse— and sometimes diverting—subjects, in his own handwriting ; and the best one can say of them is that they fulfilled their purpose as " mental exercises." It is an interesting memento of an intensely earnest little group of young men taking counsel together. In 1818 he gave up his lecturing before the City Philosophical Society. " I retire," he said in his last address, " gratified by the considerations that every lecture has tended to draw closer the ties of friendship and good feeling between the members of the Society and myself ; that each one of them has shown the advantages and uses of the Society ; and still more, by the consciousness that I have endeavoured to do, and the belief that I have done, my duty to the Society, to myself, and to you." As examples of his clearer and maturing style, we may scan a passage from one of his later lectures. He talked to the members on " The Inertia of the Mind " on July 1, 1818, and said :

" What, then (in the name of Improvement I ask it), what is the reason that, with all these facilities, without a single apparent difficulty, we are destitute in subject and meagre in interest ? Alas ! It must be apathy ; that minister of ignorance has spread his wing over us, and we shrink into indolence. Our efforts are opposed by his power, and, aided by our mean sensations of ease, he triumphs over our better judgment, and thrusts it down to contempt. And is it possible that a being endowed with such high capabilities as man, and destined to such eminent purposes, should see his powers withered, his object unattained, through the influence of that mean thing, habit, and *still*

77

remain content ? Can it be that the *degradation* and a *consciousness* of it exist at one and the same time in the same thing ? Or is apathy so powerful an agent in self-complacency that conviction is put to flight, and allowed no place in the breast ? Whatever be the reason, the melancholy truth is evident, that we are fit for the noblest purposes, but that we fulfil them not."

This is sound prose, and the whole homily carries with success a steady, cumulative argument. The reason for this is that he was very keen just now on elocution ; he reported at great length—over a hundred pages—some lectures on oratory by Mr. B. H. Smart, under whom, a few years later, he studied attentively in order to improve his vocabulary and delivery. In contrast to some of the idealism of the address just quoted comes an exceedingly practical comment which might be the forerunner of the modern " suggestion box " installed at certain large industrial works :

" Whilst passing through manufactories, and engaged in the observance of the various operations in civilised life, we are con-

stantly hearing observations made by those who find employment in those places, and are accustomed to a minute observation of what passes before them, which are new or frequently discordant with received opinions. These are generally the result of facts, and though some are founded in error, some on prejudice, yet many are true and of high importance to the practical man. Such as come in my way I shall set down here, without waiting for the principle on which they depend ; and though three-fourths of them ultimately prove to be erroneous, yet if but one new fact is gathered in a multitude, it will be sufficient to justify this mode of occupying time."

Faraday's correspondence now became less expansive, limited more to special occasions ; his letters were no longer essays on morality and mental deportment. Dr. Bence Jones puts it neatly : " There was a great change in his leisure ; there was no change in his friendliness." His contributions to the *Quarterly Journal of Science* in 1818 dealt with the combustion of the diamond, the solution of silver in ammonia, phosphorus, combinations of ammonia with chlorides, and the sounds produced by flame in tubes — not one dealt with electricity. But electricity was not forgotten ; in a letter to a doctor at South Molton, whom he had met when visiting his friend Huxtable, he describes the charging of a Leyden jar with electricity drawn from the atmosphere by the primitive means of an insulated wire up the chimney terminating in a brush of wire elevated into the air on a wooden rod ; from this he obtained sparks a quarter of an inch long.   He recommends the doctor, who was evidently electrically sympathetic, to make a simple apparatus of this kind : " It would be a constant source of interesting matter," he says, " only take care you do not kill yourself, or knock down the house."

In 1818 began a correspondence with Professor de la Rive,[1] generally upon scientific matters, which was continued with his son Auguste de la Rive, the series of letters covering thirty-eight years.   Faraday was

[1]Of Geneva ; physician, chemist, aristocrat.   His son, who lived till 1873, at the age of 22 became Professor of Natural Philosophy in the Academy of Geneva, and made electricity his principal study.

now making a name for himself in the learned world, and the older generation, contemporaries of Davy, began to regard his opinions with respect. A walking tour in Wales, beginning in July, 1819, gives him opportunity for several long descriptive entries in the journal he kept ; his sense of delight in scenery, and, better still perhaps, his sense of humour, which so far I have emphasised insufficiently, are here clearly shown. There are, of course, the usual solemn interludes, but they seem less over-powering. The first couple of pages, in which he describes the start and some of his travelling companions, are too good to miss :

" The Regulator is an excellent coach. I mounted the top of it at the ' White Horse,' Piccadilly, and it set me down in Bristol about 10 o'clk the same evening. The company upon it was not very remarkable. I came first in contact with two elderly, goodmeaning, clumsy persons, the one of whom had been showing the other his friend the town. To do this, he had taken him to the gallery of Covent Garden Theatre the night before, where they had seen something they could not describe to me ; they had then gone home, smoked pipes, and drank beer and spirits, 'till between 2 and 3 o'clk ; and then by sleeping in their chairs had passed the time until a quarter before 5 in the morning, when they mounted the coach in the city for a journey to Bristol : and now the country mouse was to entertain the city one, and return in kind the attentions he had received. I was amused and plagued all the morning by these folks ; for one of them made me laugh with his good humour and simplicity ; and the other thumped me into a mummy with his sleepy nodding. I managed to get clear of them at dinner time, or rather after dinner, by mounting on the front part of the coach, to the inconvenience of several bandboxes, and the displeasure of two ladies ; whom however I contrived to conciliate, by taking charge of a box containing a new and favourite hat."

The journal of this tour, with that of his Continental travel—both being bound within the same covers—fills hundreds of pages of exquisitely neat handwriting.

Chemistry was still his chief preoccupation, and how full his time was a letter to Abbott tells us :

" On Monday evening there is a scientific meeting of members here, and every other Monday a dinner, to both of which my company is requisite. On Tuesday evening I have a pupil, who comes at six o'clock and stops till nine, engaged in private lessons. On Wednesday the Society requires my aid. Thursday is my only evening for accidental engagements. Friday, my pupil returns and stops his three hours ; and on Saturday I have to arrange my little private business."

" If it were desirable to fix any date when the scientific education of Faraday might be said to have ended, and his work as an educated man of science might be said to have begun," writes his biographer, " it would be at the beginning of this period "—that is, the year 1820, when he reached the age of twenty-nine. " For seven years as the private assistant of Davy, and as assistant in the laboratory and lecture-room at the Royal Institution, he had now served his apprenticeship to science. He had begun a most laborious original investigation with Mr. James Stodart on the alloys of steel, which he was now about to publish."

Thirty-seven articles by him had appeared in the *Quarterly Journal* ; his lectures at the City Philosophical Society had made him well known ; and in 1821 he constructed a small piece of apparatus which was virtually the first electric motor—a laboratory trifle of wire which spun round over a magnet—small, but significant. It was time, we may think, that matters other than scientific should occupy his mind—the preoccupations which come in due course to every normally constituted youth. And in due course they did arrive—there was a love affair, carried through, as we might anticipate, most decorously ; none the less one which deserves a section of this brief chronicle for its adequate understanding, for twenty-eight years after his marriage Faraday was able to write that it was " an event which more than any other contributed to his earthly happiness and healthful state of mind."

CHAPTER SEVEN

Love and Marriage

ROMANCE, "spiritual electricity," as
Carlyle termed it, came into the life of
young Michael Faraday, but the story of his
falling in love gives us no epic of the passions. He appears never to have been in
that wondrous state of youth when the whole
world is a mystery and a glory and a dream ;
he never "plays truant from earth, slips
through the wicket of fancy into heaven's
meadow, and goes gathering stars." There
is no idyll such as that of André Marie
Ampère, the Faraday of France, courting
pretty little Julie Carron in the orchard at
Lyons, climbing cherry trees, making verses,
forgetting his umbrella, and jotting down in
his diary the transcendent trifles that shape
the lover's world. "She accepted a lily
from my hand," wrote Ampère on Monday,
July 3, 1797 ; "and then we went to see
the brook. I gave her my hand to climb
the little wall, and both hands to get over it

again." He tells how the sunset " gilded her clothes with a charming light," and " she carried away a second lily which I gave her in passing." There is no picture such as that of seventeen-year-old Benjamin Franklin walking along Market Street, Philadelphia, his pockets stuffed with shirts and stockings, eating one roll and carrying two others, one under each arm, quizzed by Miss Deborah Read as he passed her father's door—the girl little thinking, as she smiled at the boy-tramp hungrily munching, with his luggage in his bulging coat, that she was to become his wife, or that this poor wayfarer would in the years to come " snatch the lightning from the skies and the sceptre from tyrants," would be acclaimed by the wise men of Europe as a revealer of the wonders of electricity, and would be one of the most famed signatories to the Articles of the Constitution of the United States.

From stories such as these a " story " can be made ; comes into being, in fact, with scarcely any need of art. From Faraday's unimpassioned courtship, however, no brilliant episodes can be gathered, no quarrels, reconciliations, flirtatious interludes. The "rustle of a robe" was never to him "the very rattle of love's musketry." The young man fell, or glided, into love in a most discreet and methodical fashion with a member of the little congregation worshipping in their unaffected way at the Sandemanian Church of Paul's Alley. Mr. Barnard, a working silversmith of Paternoster Row, and an elder of that community, had two sons, Edward and George, both friends of Faraday, and three daughters. About this time Faraday, with the superb confidence of youth, had been making, as we have seen, depreciatory references to love in his commonplace book. "What is love?" he wrote. "A nuisance to everybody but the parties concerned. A private affair which everyone but those concerned wishes to make public." Sarah Barnard, then aged 21, had heard from her brother Edward of these captious comments in the young scientist's notebook upon the objectionable custom of falling in love. It is not unlikely that this supposed opposition to the tender passion, in one whom she was bound to meet fairly often, inspired that very passion in her—if so placid an emotion can claim so storm-tossed a name ; and although in those days maidens did not challenge their young men friends with phrases borrowed from American slang, nor call them heartily " old thing," and other abrupt endearing terms, Sarah had her share of enterprise. She asked Michael to show her certain rhymes on love of which, most fortunately as it happened, he had been guilty. In reply he sent to her a " poem " which Professor Silvanus P. Thompson published for the first time in his short biography of Faraday (1901). Of this I may give one verse, merely observing that what Faraday lacked in the arts of poesy he fully made up in other ways :

" If you urge it I cannot refuse your request :
    Though to grant it will punish severely
      my crime :
  But my fault I repent, and my errors detest;
    And I hoped to have shown my con-
      version in time."

The young lady's quiet charms, like pale flowers, strewed the scientific way, and the young man gathered them, an earnest lover, but mixing his science with his love in a most astonishing manner. For the time his sense of humour apparently deserted him. Here, dated December 1821, is an extraordinary love-letter :

ROYAL INSTITUTION,
Tuesday evening.

" MY DEAR SARAH,—It is astonishing how much the state of the body influences the powers of the mind. I have been thinking all the morning of the very delightful and interesting letter I would send you this evening, and now I am so tired, and yet have so much to do, that my thoughts are quite giddy, and run round your image without any power of themselves to stop and admire it. I want to say a thousand kind and, believe me, heartfelt things to you, but am not master of words fit for the purpose ; and still, as I ponder and think on you, chlorides, trials, oil, Davy, steel, miscellanea, mercury, and fifty other professional fancies swim before and drive me farther and farther into the quandary of stupidness.

" Ever your affectionate,
" MICHAEL."

89

Probably the young lady found this " delightful and interesting," even if the " chlorides " puzzled her. But Faraday could do better than this ; and though the correspondence of that day reminds us of the effusion of some " polite letter-writer," we cannot help liking the sincere entreaty, the " distant reverence " of the devout lover, in this little message :

" In whatever way I can best minister to your happiness either by assiduity or by absence, it shall be done. Do not injure me by withdrawing your friendship, or punish me for aiming to be more than a friend by making me less ; and if you cannot grant me more, leave me what I possess, but hear me."

He is near to poetry there—much nearer than ever he was in his rhymes ; the thirst of the lover for the beloved is in that appeal.

On August 8, 1820, he wrote :

" Since the week I have passed with you, every moment offers me fresh proof of the power you have over me. I could not at one time have thought it possible that I, that any man, could have been under the dominion of feelings so undivided and so intense ; now I think that no other man can have felt or feel as I do."

Which last phrase places Faraday, however sober his love-making may seem to us, amid the great company of lovers whose song ever has the same burden—that never before has there been a love like unto this. And once, at least, we see him at his lady's feet.

" What can I call myself," he asks, " to convey most perfectly my affection and love to you ? Can I, or can truth, say more than that for this world I am yours ? "

Sarah Barnard showed the second letter we have quoted to her father, who rather unsympathetically remarked that " love makes philosophers say many foolish things." Michael, however, had made his choice, once and for all. The course of love met with no very serious obstacles ; there was no understanding, as between Benjamin Franklin and Deborah Read, that success should come before wedding bells ; and his letters are full of dignified affection. " Ever, my dear girl, one who is perfectly yours," he signs himself. The young lady went to Ramsgate with her married sister for a change, and for a little meditation upon the position ; her suitor followed. They went for walks, visited Dover, and Faraday jots down a few revised ideas upon love in his journal ; Sarah Barnard, fit mate for him perhaps beyond all women, was won, after a period of hesitation which was by no means coyness, but a sincere deliberation upon the truth and depth of her own feelings. She was, as far as we can see, just an ordinary girl ; yet for him she was one of those " mysterious priestesses, in whose hand was the invisible Jacob's ladder, whereby man might mount into very heaven." They were married on June 12, 1821, and in every way the union was ideal. A month before his marriage he showed himself as practical as ever ; he sent to Miss Jane Barnard, his future sister-in-law, a gift—not a box of chocolates, but a workbox !

The young couple received the consent of those in authority at the Royal Institution that they should live in rooms beneath that august roof. At the same time Faraday's

position was improved. Instead of being
"lecture assistant," he became superintendent of the house and laboratory—
though his official salary reached only £100
a year.

His letters to Mrs. Faraday show that his
restless mind found in her a wonderful peace.
" Nothing rests me so much as communion
with you," he wrote, when away for a while
at the Liverpool Meeting of the British
Association in 1837. " I feel it even now as
I write, and I catch myself saying the words
aloud as I write them, as if you were within
hearing. Dear girl, think of me till Saturday evening. . . ." Twenty, thirty years
after the days of courting his letters are just
as full of affection. In 1848 he writes from
Birmingham : " What happiness is ours !
My runs into the world in this way only
serve to make me esteem that happiness
the more. . . . Write to me, dearest.
I shall get your letter on Saturday morning, or perhaps before. Love to father,
Margery, Jenny, and a thousand loves to
yourself, dearest, from your affectionate
husband."

The marriage was childless ; but Faraday's joy in children found its satisfaction, as far as might be, in the company of his nephews and nieces, who returned very thoroughly his strong affection.

CHAPTER EIGHT

The Climax : 1821–1831

FARADAY'S first paper before the Royal Society was read in 1821, the subject being exclusively chemical. About this time he was busy investigating the processes of steel manufacture, with the hope of improving them, trying, in a long series of experiments, the effect of various alloys ; but electricity and its applications came to the front in a misunderstanding which arose between him and Dr. Wollaston, who was the first person to entertain the possibility of electro-magnetic rotation. "If I understand aright," wrote Faraday to Mr. Stodart on October 8, 1821, " I am charged (1) with not acknowledging the information I received in assisting Sir H. Davy in his experiments on this subject ; (2) with concealing the theory and views of Dr. Wollaston ; (3) with taking the subject whilst Dr. Wollaston was at work on it ; and (4) with dishonourably taking Dr. Wollaston's thoughts, and pursuing them, without acknowledgment, to the results I have brought out." These charges he disproved circumstantially ; he also wrote to Dr. Wollaston requesting an interview, receiving in reply a " don't worry " sort of letter, within measurable distance of a snub. The older man, an eminent chemist and mineralogist, was probably nettled at Faraday's rather portentous apology and defence. The matter dragged on, and is not now very important, but it serves to remind us that to some extent Faraday's honours were questioned, and that others were investigating the same phenomena, endeavouring to throw light upon the same mysteries. Wollaston visited the laboratory more than once to see the experiments. Nearly two years after the letter quoted above, Faraday alluded to " the kindness and liberality of Dr. Wollaston which has been constant throughout the whole of this affair." To think evil of anyone was antipathetic to his nature ; but he could bristle angrily when any suspicion was whispered against his own integrity. He was particularly annoyed over this unpleasant interlude because it happened just when his name was before the Royal Society as a candidate for Fellowship. " I do not believe that anyone willingly was the cause of this state of things," he said, " but all seemed confusion, and generally to my disadvantage."

He was elected F.R.S. in January, 1824, at the age of thirty-three.[1] Davy was then forty-six, and the relations of the two men underwent a change. The exact position between them is obscure ; one may best express it, perhaps, as an old friendship strained by a touch of jealousy—the pupil himself now being a man of science whose words were treated with respect, well on the way to outstrip his master. Dr. Bence Jones says definitely, " That Sir H. Davy actively opposed Faraday's election is no less certain than it is sad ; " Faraday records that one of his proposers told him how Davy " walked for an hour round the courtyard of Somerset

---

[1] The Royal Society was incorporated by Royal Charter in 1663 as " The Royal Society of London for the advancement of Natural Science." Its first meetings were held in Gresham College.

House arguing " against his election ; and further evidence is provided by his own words to a friend in after years :

" Sir H. Davy told me I must take down my certificate.   I replied that I had not put it up ; that I could not take it down, as it was put up by my proposers.   He then said I must get my proposers to take it down.   I answered that I knew they would not do so. Then he said, I as President will take it down.   I replied that I was sure Sir H. Davy would do what he thought was for the good of the Royal Society."

A delightful way of " turning the other cheek "—and probably of irritating Sir Humphry still more !

At the bottom of it all was the fact that Faraday's work in the laboratory of the Royal Institution, during Davy's absence from town in the early part of 1823, gave results for which Davy wished to assume the credit. The subject on which they were both engaged was the condensation of gases, and when, much later, the *Life of Davy* appeared, Faraday defended himself from certain passages which he regarded as mis-statements by

an article in the *Philosophical Magazine* for
1836. And as, in the course of the year
1823, he discovered that after all the pother
neither he nor Davy could claim the merit for
first condensing chlorine and other gases,
but that it had been done nearly twenty years
before, " I hastened," he said, " to perform
what I thought right, and had great pleasure
in spontaneously doing justice and honour to
those who deserved it." This he did by a
paper in the *Quarterly Journal of Science*,
in 1824—honest as ever, anxious as ever to
be absolutely " straight." The friendship
of the two, however, was not gravely affected
by this interlude of disagreement.

Some of his experiments were dangerous,
and it is a wonder he was not blinded by the
explosions which occurred. One of them
drove pieces of glass " like pistol-shot "
through a window and filled his eyes with
tiny fragments ; another burned him, but
not seriously. Less risky, and more along
the lines of thought which carry his name
into every electrical text-book of the twen-
tieth century, were the experiments he began
to make on the interaction of magnetism and

electricity and on electro-magnetic induction. He had arrived at the stage when he could criticise Ampère for setting too high a value upon theory unsupported by experimental evidence—a criticism which he immediately modified, however ; and from the year 1821 we begin to see him more steadily pre-occupied with the phenomena of electricity.

In 1825 he was appointed Director of the Laboratory, " with the cordial concurrence of the board," under the superintendence of the Professor of Chemistry, W. T. Brande, F.R.S.,[1] and one of his first acts was to initiate evening meetings of the members for the discussion of scientific subjects, first in the laboratory, later in the theatre, with ladies admitted to the gallery—the fore-runners of the Friday evening discourses which are a classic of the Royal Institution. He also began the Christmas lectures to boys and girls which are now an annual and de-lightful event, and continued to lecture regularly in the mornings. One important

[1] Editor of the *Dictionary of Science and Art*. Faraday was associated with Brande in the Lectures and in editing the *Quarterly Journal*.

research in which he bore a chief share related to improvements in the manufacture of glass for optical purposes. The committee formed to advance this object reported very favourably upon " the telescope made with Mr. Faraday's glass," and recommended " that Mr. Faraday be requested to make a perfect piece of glass of the largest size that his present apparatus will admit," also that he should " teach some person to manufacture the glass for general sale "—which sounds a trifle cool, considering the abundant technical difficulties. Faraday, without saying so, seems to have thought it too much, for in replying to the Secretary of the Royal Society, Dr. Roget, he says, " Thanks— but I'd rather not," in the polished phrases of his most gracious style :

" With reference to the request which the Council of the Royal Society have done me the honour of making—namely, that I should continue the investigation—I should, under circumstances of perfect freedom, assent to it at once ; but obliged as I have been to devote the whole of my spare time to the experiments already described, and conse-

quently to resign the pursuit of such philosophical inquiries as suggested themselves
to my own mind, I would wish, under
present circumstances, to lay the glass aside
for a while, that I may enjoy the pleasure of
working out my own thoughts on other subjects.

" If at a future time the investigation
should be renewed, I must beg it to be clearly
understood, I cannot promise full success
should I resume it : all that industry and my
abilities can effect shall be done ; but to
perfect a manufacture is what I am not bold
enough to promise."

For these researches a room with special
furnaces was built at the Royal Institution.

The transition from obscurity was now
complete ; the bookbinder nears his professorship, corresponds with men of mark,
finds his name appearing on the rolls of the
scientific societies of Europe. He is still
a poor man ; he seems determined to evade
the wealth which from this time might have
been his for the taking. He declines the
Chair of Chemistry in the recently-founded
University of London, considering it a
matter of gratitude and duty to devote him-

self to the Royal Institution, in spite of a ridiculously small salary. He accepts the position of lecturer to the cadets at the Royal Academy of Woolwich, suggesting £200 as a remuneration for twenty lectures in a year. Ampère, in 1830, writes thanking him for his work in electro-magnetism—Ampère, fifty-five, grateful to Faraday, thirty-nine. And, not of least interest to us in our search for Faraday the man in Faraday the scientist, it is on record that there were many jolly evenings at the Institution in those days. Mr. George Barnard, Mrs. Faraday's youngest brother, used often to dine there, and after dinner, he says : " We nearly always had our games just like boys— sometimes at ball, or with horse chestnuts instead of marbles—Faraday appearing to enjoy them as much as I did, and generally excelling us all. Sometimes we rode round the theatre on a velocipede, which was then a new thing." Mr. D. J. Blaikley, who married the younger sister of Miss Jane Barnard, Faraday's niece, and who pre- sented many valuable documents belonging originally to the family to the Institution of

Electrical Engineers in 1915, said in his address on that occasion : " I was at the Royal Institution in Faraday's rooms on the occasion of a juvenile party, when, after various childish games and amusements, he took us all down to the lecture theatre, allowed us to play romps round the gallery, and then showed us a number of most interesting experiments." They made up river-parties, had picnics in the country, and sketching trips ; they met as friends Turner, Landseer, and other celebrated artists ; they were on good terms with famous singers and musicians. It was by no means all work and no play. But, as far as we can see, it was, for, Faraday, too much work and not enough play, not enough rest and recreation ; for his letters, even twenty years before his death, begin to contain references to his failing memory ; and as the years go on he often mentions his " stupid mind," his weariness, his state of " mental muddiness " ; his ideas grow confused, and we shall see that often only with a determined effort did he carry on his routine. He rarely appears to have taken a thorough holiday, to have set aside entirely his sense of responsibility ; and for this too steadfast application of his mind he suffered in the end. But the end is not in sight ; we are yet to see the climax of his work, the series of experiments which he carried to a triumphant conclusion in 1831, with a magnificent concentration, a rare power of eliminating unessentials, and a mind clear as crystal. Let us look at this memorable period of research a little more closely.

Since 1824 he had held the belief that as a current of electricity can cause a piece of soft iron to become a magnet, so, somehow, a magnet *ought* to be able to cause a current of electricity, or in some way, at any rate, to affect an existing current. But, try as he would—and he tried several times during the intervening years—the expected, the logical event, would not happen. In 1831 he succeeded. Ampère had caused electricity to produce magnetic effects and magnets ; Faraday now, by means of magnets, elicited electrical action. This foreshadowed another crowning feat, the exposition of the inductive effects of electrical currents—that is, more simply worded, the fact that a current flowing through one wire causes or "induces" another current to flow through another wire near it, but not in any way directly connected with it. In December, 1824, he tried to obtain an electric current by means of a magnet closely approached to a wire, and on three occasions had made elaborate but unsuccessful attempts to produce a current in one wire either by means of a current in another wire or by a magnet.

He persevered in spite of his disappointments, and on August 29, 1831, he obtained the first evidence that an electric current can induce another current in a different and unconnected circuit. Writing to a friend, on September 23, he says : " I am busy just now again on electro-magnetism, and think I have got hold of a good thing, but can't say. It may be a weed instead of a fish that, after all my labours, I may at last pull up." Had he been able to foresee how these comparatively few weeks of work would revolutionise the world of electrical science and of industry in general, even his unfailing modesty might have been pardoned for yielding, for once, to a sense of pride and elation. In nine more days he arrived at definite results, and he described the whole series of epoch-making experiments in his first " Experimental Researches," read before the Royal Society on November 24 of the same year.

Epoch-making, because the principles and reactions which Faraday discovered, examined, and proved, are fundamental ; they are the corner-stone of the vast electrical industry, and the basis of the immensely elaborate electrical generating machinery of to-day. Developed, but not unrecognisably, by very many gifted scientists in the intervening years, worked out in terms of mechanism by many skilled engineers, brought to theoretical perfection by many mathematicians, they are applied in the lighting of our homes, streets, docks, warehouses, railways ; in the running of every Tube train, and in electrically-controlled signalling systems, in the ignition system of innumerable motor-car and aeroplane engines ; latest of all, they are the principles

upon which wireless reception is founded.
The great point, as we saw in our first
chapter, was that the flow of current produced
in a wire by the approach of a magnet was a
momentary one, followed by a second momentary flow in the opposite direction when the
magnet was removed ; hitherto this had un-
accountably been missed. And the electricity which we use to-day, distributed in
every town by street mains as common as
gas or water mains, is, in popular language,
nothing but the production of these momentary currents with such extreme rapidity
than when collected by suitable mechanism
they are indistinguishable from a perfectly
steady flow. That the machinery and the
many devices in this process are now in-
credibly ingenious and often extremely com-
plex does not alter the fundamental principle,
the discovery of which we owe to the genius
of Michael Faraday. The first primitive
revolving " motors " of his own design are
the progenitors of the dynamo of the eighties
and the giant turbo-generators of the present
day. I give here, for their historical interest,
a few sentences from two paragraphs in

which he describes electrical induction and the experiment with a magnet :

" 1. When an electric current is passed through one of two parallel wires, it causes at first a current in the same direction through the other, but this induced current does not last a moment, notwithstanding the inducing current (from the voltaic battery) is continued ; all seems unchanged, except that the principal current continues its course. But when the current is stopped,[1] then a return current occurs in the wire under induction, of about the same intensity and momentary duration, but in the opposite direction to that first formed. . . .

" 2. Then I found that magnets would induce just like voltaic currents, and by bringing helices and wires up to the poles of magnets, electrical currents were produced in them ; these currents being able to deflect the galvonometer, or to make, by means of the helix, magnetic needles, or in one case even to give a spark. Hence the evolution of *electricity from magnetism*. The currents were not permanent. They ceased the moment the wires ceased to approach the magnet, because the new and apparently quiescent state was assumed, just as in the

---

[1] That is, the principal or original current.—W.L.R.

case of the induction of currents. But when the magnet was removed, and its induction therefore ceased, the return currents appeared as before."

The two kinds of induction Faraday called "volta-electric" and "magneto-electric," and considered their identity of action and results a very powerful proof of Ampère's theory of magnetism.

He continued experimenting with the effects of the earth's magnetism, using an iron disc, a copper plate, a brass shell, and other devices. In a glass case at the Royal Institution many of his original pieces of apparatus are preserved, in practically perfect condition—the first induction coil or transformer, and other electro-magnetic experimental models. On a pedestal in the same room stands his big electro-magnet, still shown occasionally at the Christmas lectures to children. The story goes that Faraday made this from part of an old anchor which he saw at the docks and purchased for a shilling or two ; quite a probable story. But the fact that he and his assistant, Anderson, covered the whole of the wire of this magnet with insulating material is of even greater interest to anyone who handles wire in these days of " wireless." There must have been a week's work in it.

Summarising this period of strenuous research, Professor Tyndall, after some rather technical paragraphs which may be omitted, has a passage bordering upon the lyrical, and curiously calling to mind the rhythm of a wonderful page in Francis Thompson's essay on " Shelley " :—

" He now passes from his little brass globe to the globe of the earth. He plays like a magician with the earth's magnetism. He sees the invisible lines along which its magnetic action is exerted, and, sweeping his wand across these lines, he evokes this new power. Placing a simple loop of wire round a magnetic needle, he bends its upper portion to the west : the point of the needle immediately swerves to the east ; he bends his loop to the east, and the needle point moves to the west. . . . And then his thoughts suddenly widen, and he asks himself whether the rotating earth does not generate induced currents as it turns round its axis from west to east."

In pursuit of this idea, " he went to the round lake near Kensington Palace, and stretched 480 feet of copper wire, north and south, over the lake, causing plates soldered to the wire at its ends to dip into the water. The copper wire was severed at the middle, and the severed ends connected with a galvanometer. No effect whatever was observed. But though quiescent water gave no effect, moving water might. He therefore worked at Waterloo Bridge for three days, during the ebb and flow of the tide, but without any satisfactory result." This was written, Professor Tyndall observes, before the submarine cable was thought of ; but Faraday once informed Tyndall that actual observation upon that cable had proved that currents such as he had expected did exist.

Still engaged upon electrical investigations, with interludes of chemical and optical work, Faraday proved the identity of electricity derived from various sources, examined its effects when applied to the production of chemical action, and arrived at a definite method of measuring the quantity of electricity evolved under certain conditions, warning himself, by an amusing note, to be practical : " I must keep my researches really *experimental*, and not let them deserve anywhere the character of *hypothetical imaginations*." The ground he covered in the work of these three or four years was astonishing in its extent. He carried on, for example, a great deal of pioneer research upon what happens when a current flows through a liquid, laid thus the foundation of electro-deposition of metals (electro-plating) and in his published accounts of these experiments used terms which are accepted by all at the present day— " electrolysis," " anode," and " cathode." The principle he established is known as Faraday's Law.

As his success became known, offers of assistance and suggestions came in great numbers from outsiders, drawing from him the dry comment that " volunteers are serious embarrassments, generally, to the experienced philosopher." We gain some idea of the strain of this period by remembering that his lecturing was still going on, and that to make a bare list of the subjects on which he spoke would fill two or three pages. They ranged from domestic themes of almost absurd simplicity—the kettle, the candle, lamps, chimneys—to the prevention of dry rot in timber ; from electricity and magnetism—many discourses on these—to " Mr. Brunel's new mode of constructing Arches for Bridges." Honours came to him unsought ; he received the D.C.L. of Oxford University, and the Copley Medal of the Royal Society. The bestowal of this medal originated in a bequest by Sir Godfrey Copley (who died in 1709) of £100 " in trust for the Royal Society of London for improving natural knowledge " ; the first award was made in 1731, the second in 1734, and in 1736 the bequest was converted into the gift of a gold medal annually. It is awarded to the living author of " such philosophical research, either published or communicated to the Society, as may appear to the Council to be deserving of that honour " ; and the recipient need not be an Englishman. Volta, for example, received it in the year of Faraday's birth. Faraday was elected member

of several foreign colleges and academies ;
he was appointed first Fullerian Professor
of Chemistry at the Royal Institution.   That
learned body wished him well, and yet could
not act up to its collective valuation of him
for the reason perceived in the following
report of a Committee on Salaries in 1832—
the year in which his paper on magneto-
electric induction was read before the Royal
Society as the Bakerian Lecture :

" The Committee are certainly of opinion
that no reduction can be made in Mr. Faraday's salary, £100 per annum, house, coals,
and candles ; and beg to express their regret
that the circumstances of the Institution are
not such as to justify their proposing such an
increase of it as the variety of duties which
Mr. Faraday has to perform, and the zeal
and ability with which he performs them,
appear to merit."

A fresh chapter of Faraday's life seems to
begin with the conclusion, or rather sus-
pension, of his electrical and magnetic experiments, and one of its opening incidents
concerns the pension which he refused and

afterwards accepted. This little story, which throws another gleam upon his almost grim independence of character, is worth a place in our consideration of the next phase of his career.

CHAPTER IX

Manifold Activities

ON April 20, 1835, Faraday was informed by Sir James South, F.R.S., one of the founders of the Royal Astronomical Society, that had Sir Robert Peel remained in office a pension would have been given him.[1] Faraday replied to the effect that he could not accept a pension while he was able to work for his living—rather ungraciously, in fact ; he modified this, on the advice of his father-in-law, by a second letter containing a less decisive refusal. The wheel of politics turned, and on October 26 he had an interview with Lord Melbourne, the Prime Minister, at the Treasury, but Lord Melbourne's bluntness seems to have displeased him, and he " respectfully declined the favour " once again. Lady Mary Fox, a friend of both the parties, tried to arrange matters smoothly ; Faraday, however, was

[1] Sir Robert Peel, on the defeat of the Government, had ceased to be Prime Minister on April 8.

piqued, and said : " I should require from his Lordship what I have no right or reason to expect that he would grant—a written apology for the words he permitted himself to use to me." Lord Melbourne, on November 24, sent a very courteous explanation, almost amounting to an apology—certainly to a regret at any misunderstanding—and Faraday capitulated in a charming little note. Unfortunately some busybody sent to *Fraser's Magazine* an account of the interview between Lord Melbourne and Faraday in which the Prime Minister is represented as saying : " I hate the name of the pension ; I look upon the whole system of giving pensions to literary and scientific persons as a piece of gross humbug." This appeared in the *Times* of November 28, and the secret is out when the heading of the imaginary dialogue is told : it was entitled " Tory and Whig Patronage to Science and Literature," and Faraday characterised it as " full of falsehood and evidently written for a factious purpose." In the *Times* of December 8 he wrote : " I beg leave thus publicly to state that neither directly nor indirectly did I communicate to the editor of *Fraser's Magazine* the information on which that article was founded," and the end of the breeze came on December 24, when the pension, of £300, was granted—and accepted, Lord Melbourne, according to a letter by Faraday of many years later, having behaved " very handsomely " in the matter.

One of Faraday's few genuine holidays was a short tour in Switzerland in the summer of this year, but it does not appear to have benefited him greatly, for, on working at electro-chemical decomposition directly after his return, he writes : " Very tired—cannot get energies up." This is the first hint of strain ; the wonder is only that he had not been compelled to rest long before. In 1836 he drew up notes for a fresh course of fourteen lectures on electricity, which he gave before the students at St. George's Hospital ; and he made, as usual, hundreds of experiments. On November 30, 1837, he sent the result of two years of hard work to the Royal Society—the eleventh series of " Experimental Researches " ; the twelfth he sent in January, 1838, the thirteenth in February,

the fourteenth in June, the fifteenth in
November. The amount of mere handwriting must have been enormous, apart from
the concentration of thought and the actual
laboratory manipulations, the basis of it all.
" It would be easy," says Professor Tyndall,
" to criticise these researches, easy to show
the looseness, and sometimes the inaccuracy,
of the phraseology employed ; but this
critical spirit will get little good out of
Faraday. . . . It must always be remem-
bered that he works at the very boundaries
of our knowledge." A prediction which he
made in one of this series of researches with
regard to the behaviour of an electric current
under certain conditions was confirmed
sixteen years later—a brilliant instance of his
uncanny power of intuition. One strange
omission strikes the reader of his letters—
the name of William Sturgeon is not mentioned. Sturgeon, from 1823 to 1840, was
doing excellent pioneer work in electro-
magnetism which proved invaluable to others
who were investigating the same field.

A new phase of his industry begins in
1836, when he became associated with

Trinity House, examining the processes of illumination in lighthouses, reporting upon various types of lamp, measuring the intensity of light given. For thirty years he held this position of adviser, or " standing counsel " as he termed it, and a passage in his reply to Captain Pelly, Deputy-Master of Trinity House, shows his indifference to mere money-making :

" In consequence of the goodwill and confidence of all around me, I can at any moment convert my time into money, but I do not require more of the latter than is sufficient for necessary purposes. The sum, therefore, of £200 is quite enough in itself, but not if it is to be the indicator of the character of the appointment ; but I think you do not view it so, and that you and I understand each other in that respect."

The years from 1841 to 1844 framed a period of less work, if not precisely of rest, and had he not taken life a little more easily only one result was possible—a complete breakdown. Danger-signals of giddiness and failing memory were being shown in sheer self-defence by his tired brain ; in

1843 he writes to Matteucci, the Italian scientist, as " one who feels as if his purpose of life in this world were passed." " Every letter of yours," he continues, " finds me withdrawn more and more. . . . My health and spirits are good, but my memory is gone, and it, like deafness, makes a man retreat into himself." To another correspondent, in the following year, he gives more particularly his sensations of lowered vitality :

" You have all the confidence of unbaulked health and youth in both body and mind ; I am a labourer of many years' standing, made daily to feel my wearing out. You, with increasing acquisition of knowledge, enlarge your views and intentions ; I, though I may gain from day to day some little maturity of thought, feel the decay of powers, and am constrained to a continual process of lessening my intentions and contracting my pursuits. Many a fair discovery stands before me in thought which I once intended, and even now desire, to work out ; but I lose all hope respecting them when I turn my thoughts to that one which is in hand, and see how slowly, for want of time and physical power, it advances. . . . You do not know how often I have to go to my medical friend to speak of giddiness and aching of the head, etc., and how often he has to bid me cease from restless thoughts and mental occupation and retire to the seaside to inaction."

This, at the age of fifty-three, was significant of the ten years of almost incessant thought and hard work which had left him exhausted. Three months in Switzerland in the summer of 1841, though thoroughly enjoyed, judging by the diary he kept, had not been able to restore full health, and at so early an age—for no man of sound constitution and assured income should despond at fifty-three—such letters read pathos into a generally cheerful life. He kept up his lectures at the Royal Institution, visited various lighthouses, and in 1842 investigated the electricity of steam-jets—quite enough to cause brain-fag in a man of less energy ; he speculated upon the nature of matter, and in 1844 turned again to one of his earliest subjects, the condensation of gases. In the autumn of that year he took part in an inquiry into the causes of a colliery explosion at Haswell, near Durham ; this lasted five days. He cross-examined the witnesses, says Sir Charles Lyell, " with as much talent, skill, and self-possession as if he had been an old practitioner at the bar." Among other questions, he asked how the rate of flow of air-currents was measured in the mine, and an inspector illustrated this by the smoke from a pinch of gunpowder which he took from a small box in his pocket and allowed to fall through the flame of a candle. Faraday was rather concerned about the casual way in which the gunpowder was handled, and asked where they kept it ; the inspector told him it was kept in a bag, the neck of which was tied tightly. " Where do you keep the bag ? " asked Faraday. " You are sitting on it," was the startling reply. As commissioner, he had been given the softest cushion available—which was the powder-bag ! He sprang up and rated the mine officials smartly for carelessness—particularly discreditable, he pointed out, in those who should be specially vigilant, being in a position to set an example to men who were in hourly danger of explosions.

To the subscription opened for the widows

and orphans left by the men who had been killed in this disaster Faraday contributed, privately, a large sum.

With the year 1845 begins a final period of brilliant research, the last steady work this " restless analyst " was to do ; but it occupied ten years. He seemed to gain a fresh grip on himself, and though he still complained of his poor memory, he was very evidently in better mental trim. For a time the danger of a breakdown was over ; his spirits had been enlivened by three years of comparative leisure—containing, however, enough scientific labour to satisfy any normal appetite. Much of this later discovery is too technical to be given here ; it related to the effect of magnetism on polarised light and the phenomena of diamagnetism—the curious property which certain substances possess of arranging themselves, when suspended between the poles of a magnet, across the line joining the poles instead of parallel with that line. For three months, in 1845, he explored this byway untiringly, sometimes ending his notes with the simple phrase : " Have done enough for to-day." Results were principally negative and not very promising ; but on November 3, a new and powerful horseshoe magnet having arrived, the indefatigable student and scholar made some fresh trials. A bar of heavy glass was suspended by silk thread between the poles. " When it was arranged, and had come to rest," he wrote, " I found I *could* affect it by the magnetic force and give it position." Though not of such far-reaching importance as his prime claim to our remembrance, the discoveries of Faraday in the sphere of the relation between light and magnetism, and diamagnetism, have been of great value and significance to science. Sir John Herschel wrote to him, congratulating him warmly upon these new labours, and Mrs. Marcet, whose *Conversations on Chemistry* had aroused in boyhood his interest, correcting the sheets of a new edition, asked him for some account of the fresh facts, to be included.

For three weeks in this year he was in France, partly to inspect some of the French lighthouses, partly to be admitted a member of the French Academy ; his wife and

Mr. G. Barnard accompanied him on this trip. In Paris he met Arago and heard him lecture.

His own lectures at the Institution continued, and there is abundant evidence that he had the power of expounding science in an exceptionally attractive manner ; so much evidence, in fact, that we feel a sense of loss in not having heard his voice, seen his ardent face, when he was engaged in this, his best-loved duty. He took for one series the common objects of the home—the " breakfast table " series—and Charles Dickens, who had just become editor of *Household Words*, asked to be allowed to publish some account of these lectures, in a letter which is a gem of courtesy from one eminent man to another. I have had the privilege of seeing this and the following letters, and they are now printed for the first time. The first is that of a respectful and admiring stranger :

DEVONSHIRE TERRACE,

Twenty-eighth May, 1850.

DEAR SIR,—I take the liberty of addressing you as if I knew you personally ; trusting

that I may venture to assume that you will
excuse that freedom.

It has occurred to me that it would be extremely beneficial to a large class of the
public to have some account of your late
lectures on the breakfast-table, and of those
you addressed, last year, to children. I
should be exceedingly glad to have some
papers in reference to them, published in my
new enterprise *Household Words*. May I ask
you whether it would be agreeable, to you,
and, if so, whether you would favour me
with the loan of your notes of those lectures
for perusal ?

I am sensible that you may have reasons
of your own, for reserving the subject to
yourself. In that case, I beg to assure you
that I would on no account approach it.

 With great respect and esteem, I am Dear
Sir
    Your faithful Servant,

      CHARLES DICKENS.

MICHAEL FARADAY, Esquire.

To this Faraday must have replied immediately, judging by the second letter dated
three days later :

Devonshire Terrace,

Thirty-First May, 1850.

My Dear Sir,—I really cannot tell you how very sensible I am of your great kindness or what an honour I feel it to be to have interested you in my books.

I think I may be able to do something with the candle ; but I would not touch it, or have it touched, unless it can be relighted with something of the beautiful simplicity and clearness of which I see the traces in your notes.

Since you are so generous as to offer me the notes of your lectures on the breakfast table, I will borrow them when you have done with them, if it be only for my own interest and gratification. I deeply regret now, not having heard the lectures to children as it would have been a perfect delight to me to have described them, however generally.

I should take it as a great favour if you could allow me (in the event of my being unfortunately unable to come myself) to introduce my sub-editor to your next lecture ; for a subsequent comparison of his recollection of it, with your notes, might enlighten us very much.

Pray let me add, as one who has long respected you, and strongly felt the obligations society owes to you, that the day on which I took the liberty of writing to you will always be a memorable day in my calendar, if I date from it—as I now hope I shall—the beginning of a personal knowledge of you.

> My dear Sir,
> Yours faithfully and obliged
>
> CHARLES DICKENS.

A third letter towards the end of the year closes this brief correspondence, as far as we can ascertain.

> DEVONSHIRE HOUSE,
> *Eleventh December*, 1850.

MY DEAR SIR,—Will you do me the favour to accept the accompanying book—a poor mark of my respect for your public character and services, and my remembrance of your private kindness in so generously lending me your valuable notes.

Concerning which, let me say that I have them in safe keeping, and will shortly return them. The gentleman who has them to refer to, still tells me when I ask if he has done with them, "that they are not easily exhausted, and that they suggest something else."

My Dear Sir,

Yours faithfully and obliged

CHARLES DICKENS.

Professor FARADAY.

There is, in the Royal Institution, a book of Faraday's which so far has never been mentioned, and which few have seen. It is known as his "Flower Book," and consists entirely of pressed flowers, leaves, and grasses, arranged with perfect taste on alternate pages. Opposite some of the flowers is a verse of poetry in Faraday's writing. This unique collection bears the inscription, "To Jane Barnard, 1850," and it came into the possession of the Institution very recently, having been presented by Mr. Evelyn Barnard last year. Even in the midst of his scientific activities, he found a little time for the making of this charming record ; it throws another pleasing gleam of light upon the man himself, and we hear the undertones which the world missed in its popular acclaim.

131

While we are bound to pass over most of the subjects of Faraday's numberless lectures without even a quotation, there is a passage in the last of a course of eight delivered in 1847 which I cannot omit, so well does it exhibit Faraday at his best :

" Our philosophy, feeble as it is, gives us to see in every particle of matter a *centre* of force reaching to an infinite distance, binding worlds and suns together, and unchangeable in its permanency. Around this same particle we see grouped the powers of all the various phenomena of nature : the heat, the cold, the wind, the storm, the awful conflagration, the vivid lightning flash, the stability of the rock and the mountain, the grand mobility of the ocean, with its mighty tidal wave sweeping round the globe in its diurnal journey, the dancing of the stream and the torrent ; the glorious cloud, the soft dew, the rain dropping fatness, the harmonious working of all these forces in nature, until at last the molecule rises up in accordance with the mighty purpose ordained for it, and plays its part in the gift of *life itself*. And therefore our philosophy, whilst it shows us these things, should lead us to think of Him who hath wrought them ; for it is said by an authority far above even that which these works present, that ' the invisible things of Him from the creation of the world are clearly seen, being understood by the things that are made, even His eternal power and Godhead.' "

In the previous year the Rumford and the Royal Medals had been awarded to him— " a double honour," says Dr. Bence Jones, " which will probably long be unique in the annals of the Royal Society." Count Benjamin Thompson, who afterward assumed the name of Rumford, is worth a brief digression, for it was he who formed the plan of the Royal Institution, Faraday's home. He was born in Massachusetts, in 1753, and had a very varied career. In 1775 he came to England as bearer of despatches to Lord George Germain, Secretary of State for the Colonies, who appointed him a clerk in the Foreign Office ; five years later he became Under-Secretary of State. He returned to America, and visited Munich in 1784, to become aide-de-camp to the reigning Prince of Bavaria. Taking the name of Rumford, from the town in America where his early life had been spent, he turned his attention to caring for the poor ; in devising means to warm and clothe the destitute he made experiments in light and heat, essays on which he published in London in 1795. Eventually, after sharing with Sir Joseph Banks an important part in founding the Royal Institution, which was incorporated by Royal Charter in the year 1800, he settled in France and married the widow of Lavoisier, the great chemist, dying at Auteuil in 1814.

Faraday's brother was killed in 1846, by an accident while driving ; the poor fellow was taken to University Hospital. " I saw the corpse this morning," wrote Faraday to his wife, " and though sadly bruised, it was just my dear brother."

The years which followed were filled with activity, but we must dismiss them briefly —our sketch of previous years must serve as a suggestion of Faraday's many notes, lectures, letters, and experiments in this period. He advised the captain of the Royal yacht, comparing paddle-wheel with screw in a clever dissertation, and he carried on several prolonged series of experiments upon crystals

and their magnetic properties. His work for Trinity House continued. He reported on such subjects as adulteration of white lead, impure oils, lenses, ventilation, fog-signals. Two systems of arc lighting were examined, but he decided against them— he " could not put up in a lighthouse what has not been established beforehand, and is only experimental." In 1856 he made five reports, in 1857 six, and in 1858 twelve, one being on the electric light at South Foreland : the tiny spark which he had produced a quarter of a century before was now the steady source of constant illumination. In 1860 he gave his verdict in favour of " magneto-electric lighting " (his own discovery, and our present generating system in its earlier stages) ; the following year he inspected the installation at Dungeness, and in 1862 he made seventeen reports. In 1863 he again visited Dungeness, and the next year supplied twelve reports and examined the plans for installing electric light at Portland. His last report for Trinity House was on the St. Bees' Light in 1865. " Without doubt," says Dr. Bence Jones,

" his frequent journeys to the South Foreland and Dungeness Lighthouses, and his night excursions in the Channel during the winter, when he was seventy years old, were remote causes of his last illness."

The letters of these years show the recurrence of his great trouble, failure of memory. " As a fresh incident creeps dimly into view," he writes to his friend Professor Schonbein, " I lose sight of the old ones, and I cannot tell how many are forgotten altogether." This was in 1855 ; and the very next year his work in the laboratory was more continuous than it had ever been. His lectures drew the highest in the land by their charm. The Prince of Wales (King Edward) wrote from Windsor Castle thanking him for them ; " I shall always cherish with great pleasure," he said, " the recollection of having been assisted in my early studies in chemistry by so distinguished a man." Even in the pages of *Punch* we find echoes of his fame. " Mary Ann's Notions " in 1857 were a kind of mid-Victorian " Belle's Letters," and the vivacious " Mary Ann " quite fell in love with him. " Do you know Dr. Faraday ? "

she asks. " I suppose so, as you know all
the clever people in the world. Isn't he a
dear ? " She appears to have thoroughly
enjoyed one of his evenings. " Prince Albert
was there, with his star on, looking so grave
and elegant . . . he listened with the utmost
steadiness, and I don't believe he moved
half or a quarter of an inch all the time. . . .
But the lecture was lovely. It was quite a
treat to look at dear Dr. Faraday's earnest
face and silvery hair ; not that he is an old
man, far from it, and he is far more light and
active than many a smoky stupid all-round
collar man that I know."

In 1860 he spent much time on one of his
pet theories, the possible connection of the
force of gravity with electricity, but without
success. By this time he was established,
owing to the thoughtfulness of Prince Albert,
in a house at Hampton Court, the Queen
having relieved all difficulties as to repairs.
And with 1861, when he wrote a touching
letter to the managers of the Royal Institution, he begins to feel that he is entering the
Valley of the Shadow, even though for a few
years more he carried on a certain amount of

scientific labour. In this very year we find a letter from " the Lords of the Committee of Council on Education," thanking him for his valuable report on the subject of lighting Picture Galleries with gas, and enclosing " the honorarium "—a cheque for five guineas ! In the original letter this amount is ringed by a pencil mark, and the word " returned " is written beneath—I think in Faraday's handwriting.

Some of the letters he received from complete strangers are highly amusing. They came by dozens, and many of them are still preserved with his papers and note-books. They show that in those days, as now, the man whose name is before the world must suffer fools more or less gladly, must pay the penalty of fame by an expanding and not very inspiring post-bag. To-day such a man is protected by a secretary who weeds out the useless letters ; Faraday, as we can tell from his pencilled comments, read his whole correspondence, though he doubtless left unanswered a large proportion of it. Sheets of paper closely written, thick as autumn leaves, fell from a lady who in 1845 besought him to try mesmerism for his health ; she was " turned down," for on the envelope of the bulky letter is the concise pencilled summary, " Mesmeric Stuff ! " Another correspondent, writing from the Conservative Club, St. James St., July 5, inquired if Faraday could give some opinion " as to the cause of the violent gales of wind which prevailed for so long a time," ascribing them himself to the continued firing at Sebastopol and " the prodigious quantity of gunpowder thus expanded into gas," and concluding pathetically : " It would very much gratify me to have your opinion on the subject in order that I may be corrected if I am wrong in my opinion but if right that I may have the opportunity of waving your letter in the faces of my friends and thereby stop that ridicule and laughter which generally accompany the expression of my opinion." One writer gives the story of his life, and encloses an extraordinary hand-written booklet entitled " Panurgon, or, A Short Essay on Cause and Effect : Being an attempt to explain the nature and causes of Light, Heat, Gravitation, Terrestrial Magnetism, &c." One admires that delightful " &c." ! A letter received in 1839 begins : " Sir,—I have considered it not impossible for to construct a machine by which we might be transported through the air with great velocity." The idea was " a hollow Sphere (with paddles fixed to it) of light material," and it " must also have a dome to prevent it neutralising its own motion "—a suggestion which probably puzzled Faraday as much as it puzzles us.

CHAPTER X

Faith and Character

PHILOSOPHIC doubt arises spontaneously in many minds that have been strictly trained in youth to accept religious dogma—strangely enough, the one thing upon which we should not dare to dogmatise or dictate ; other minds, trained with equal love and care and strictness, rest calmly within a faith inherited or conferred. They refuse, they do not need, to wrestle with the angel " until the breaking of the day " ; they see shining—and happy are they so to see—

> ". . . the traffic of Jacob's ladder
> Pitched betwixt Heaven and Charing
> Cross."

They leave to others the splendid doubts, the mental conflicts, which if they have left unmoved the mists which hide the truth itself, have yet by their very urgency lifted the human spirit from the stagnation of unruffled acquiescence, and have given the world some of its finest literature, because of the irresistible conviction that only by searching can man find out God, or truth. It is a matter of temperament ; and each side, philosophy and religion—not necessarily antagonists—has moved the world.

" There is no philosophy in my religion," wrote Faraday, at the age of fifty-three, to a lady who wished to associate herself with him in his work ; and then seems to disprove his assertion by continuing :

" I should be glad to think that high mental powers insured something like a high moral sense, but have often been grieved to see the contrary, as also on the other hand my spirit has been cheered by observing in some lowly and uninstructed creature such a healthful and honourable and dignified mind as made one in love with human nature. . . . . I am of a very small and despised sect of Christians, known, if known at all, as Sandemanians, and our hope is founded on the faith that is in Christ. But though the natural works of God can never by any possibility come in contradiction with the higher things that belong to our future existence, and must with everything concerning him ever glorify Him, still I do not think it at all necessary to tie the study of

the natural sciences and religion together,
and, in my intercourse with my fellow-
creatures, that which is religious and that
which is philosophical have ever been two
distinct things."

Calm, honest, unaffected faith is the note of
all the letters in which religious matters are
touched upon, and there is not the faintest
doubt of his absolute sincerity.

This simple faith, expressed in the simplest form of public worship, in which
Faraday's early years had been spent, he
retained unquestioningly throughout his
whole life ; which is the more remarkable,
to us, since his general tendency was to
depart from accepted beliefs, to trace for
himself independent and adventurous ways,
and almost to worship facts. " I could
trust a fact," he said, " and always cross-
examined an assertion." Acute though he
showed himself to be, however, when on the
trail of some scientific quarry, his essentially
kindly and unassuming soul never, if we may
so put it, started the smallest hare of doubt
on the spiritual course ; nor, if it had done
so, can we imagine him pursuing it. To

many his creed may be a cage, a prison,
provocative of the beating and breaking of
bars ; to him it was a pillow, providing
rest.

The sect of Sandemanians or " Glassites "
to which Faraday's parents belonged, has
never been powerful, neither John Glass,
its founder, nor Robert Sandeman his son-
in-law, its later head, having taken the world
by storm, though in the Scottish Church
their restless behaviour provoked waves of
disturbance strong enough to wash them
safely ashore in biographical dictionaries
and the memoirs of their period. Glas, or
Glass, was born in Fifeshire in 1695 ; he
became a minister of the Presbyterians in
1719, and seems to have been a popular
preacher. Six years later he formed a
society numbering about a hundred members
in his parish at Tealing, Forfarshire, who
gathered together once a month for celebra-
tion of the Lord's Supper and the attainment
of " closer religious fellowship "—the little
break-away bearing a remarkable resem-
blance in essentials to that of John Wesley at
Oxford University a very few years after-

ward. Regarded by his spiritual elders as a
dangerous person by reason of his inexplicable dissatisfaction, also incurring their displeasure with regard to other matters—
which included the inevitable pamphlet of
those days—he was suspended, and deprived
of his office in 1728. He approached what
to us may resemble the wintry chill of Cal-
vinism ; but in this we may do him an injustice. One of his beliefs was the perpetua-
tion of the " kiss of peace " ; another was
the meal in common—the " love-feast,"
perhaps, of the later Methodists. He founded
a church at Dundee, and died in 1773.

Robert Sandeman, also a Scottish divine,
was born at Perth in 1723, and educated at
St. Andrews ; he carried on the cause by
marrying the daughter of Glass, and apparently changed its name as well as hers, for he
became the recognised chief of the small
body of followers under his guidance—the
" Sandemanians." In 1760, London having
called him, he formed a little congregation at
Glovers Hall, Beech Lane, Barbican, re-
moving the scene after a while to a building
in St. Martin's-le-Grand, formerly a Friends'

meeting-house. Desiring to extend the peculiar department of belief which he had adopted, he sailed from Glasgow to Boston, on missionary enterprise bent, in 1764. In New England he appears to have met with some success, for he remained in America until his death, in Connecticut, in 1771— a year or so before that of the original founder of the little band.

How was it, we may be permitted to wonder, that an intellect so alive and alert as Michael Faraday's, accustomed to probe all fair-seeming hypotheses, demanding with the utmost exigence faultless and repeated proofs of any scientific theory before he accepted it, could rest so contentedly, even with happy and active participation, in so uncultured a fold? We shall find some answer to the question as we look at him more closely. " A month after his marriage," records Dr. Bence Jones, " he made his confession of sin and profession of faith before the Sandemanian Church." This was one of the conditions of full reception into the sect. " His faith in Christ he considered to be the effect of Divine power—the un-

merited gift of God to one who had nothing
in him that could be pleasing in His sight.
The sense of his own unworthiness, and in-
capability of doing what was good before
God, extended even to this act of professing
the truth. When his wife asked him why
he had not told her what he was about to do,
he only replied, ' That is between me and
my God.' " And remarkably patient the
newly-wed wife must have been to accept
such a snub—one is almost tempted to
accuse her husband of spiritual snobbiness—
without protest ; though the tone of voice,
the glance, the manner, which may have
modified it, to us are lost. " When he
entered the meeting-house," continues his
friend and biographer, " he left his science
behind, and he would listen to the prayer and
exhortation of the most illiterate brother of
his sect with an attention which showed how
he loved the word of truth, from whomsoever
it came."

Fluent in speech, and abounding in ideas,
in his scientific discourses, he retained his
fluency, but was very lacking in ideas when
as an elder of the Sandemanian company he

preached and exhorted the brethren on alternate Sundays. This he did for three years and a-half from 1840, having already spoken occasionally at week-day meetings. " His sermons were always extemporary," says Dr. Bence Jones, " but they were prepared with great care. There was no eloquence. There was not one word said for effect. The overflowing energy and clearness of the lecture-room were replaced by an earnestness of manner best summed up in the word devoutness. His object seemed to be to make the most use of the words of Scripture, and to make as little of his own as he could. Hence a stranger was struck first by the number and rapidity of his references to texts in the Old and New Testaments, and secondly by the devoutness of his manner." A friend who once heard him records that " he read a long portion of one of the gospels slowly, reverently, and with such an intelligent and sympathising appreciation of the meaning that I thought I had never heard before so excellent a reader." When away from home, he kept in touch with the Sandemanians of other towns. " I well remember," said Lord Kelvin, " at meetings of the British Association in Aberdeen and Glasgow, how he sought out the meetings of his denomination, and spent, as a preacher or worshipper there, the Sunday and any time he could spare from the work of the Association."

Faraday's own words will serve to explain his attitude in these matters more clearly than any attempts of our own at analysis. There is a noble and earnest passage at the end of his *Researches in Chemistry and Physics* which goes far to interpret the unfaltering fairness and beauty of his life, and at the same time gives us a glimpse into a mind clear as a woodland pool, and perfectly aware of possible reproaches :

" I believe that as man is placed above the creatures round him, there is a higher and far more exalted position within his view ; and the ways are infinite in which he occupies his thoughts about the fears, or hope, or expectations, of a future life. I believe that the truth of that future cannot be brought to his knowledge by any exertion of his mental powers, however exalted they may be ;

that it is made known to him by other teaching than his own ; it is received through simple belief of the testimony given. Let no one suppose, for an instant, that the self-education I am about to commend, in respect of the things of this life, extends to any considerations of the hope set before us, as if man by reasoning could find out God. It would be improper here to enter upon this subject farther than to claim an absolute distinction between religious and ordinary belief. I shall be reproached with the weakness of refusing to apply those mental operations which I think good in respect of high things to the very highest. I am content to bear the reproach. . . . I have never seen anything incompatible between those things of man which can be known by the spirit of man which is within him and those higher things concerning his future, which he cannot know by that spirit."

This finely-uttered passage, showing that he recognised the problem his attitude presented to others, occurred in a lecture on " Mental Education " delivered before the Royal Institution on May 6, 1854, at which the Prince Consort, a great admirer of Faraday, was a member of the audience. It was afterwards reprinted in *Researches on Chemistry and Physics*. Its words and their burden " are so immediately connected in their nature and origin with my own experimental life," wrote Faraday, " considered either as cause or consequence, that I have thought the close of this volume not an unfit place for their reproduction."

To such a mind, so strongly set on seeing those things which are invisible, so easily able to climb peaks of faith inaccessible to others, the phenomena of spiritualism would naturally cause impatience. " Table-turning " made rather a sensation, and proved useful at least in filling a good many newspaper columns, in the summer of 1853, and Faraday entered the controversy. " I have not been at work except in turning the tables upon the table-turners," he wrote to Professor Schonbein on July 25, " nor should I have done that, but that so many inquiries poured in upon me that I thought it better to stop the inpouring flood by letting all know at once what my views and thoughts were." And he effervesces into something as near derision as any words he ever wrote :

" What a weak, credulous, incredulous, unbelieving, superstitious, bold, frightened, what a ridiculous world ours is, as far as concerns the mind of man. How full of inconsistencies, contradictions, and absurdities it is. I declare that, taking the average of many minds that have recently come before me (and apart from that spirit which God has placed in each) and accepting for a moment that average as a standard, I should far prefer the obedience, affections, and instinct of a dog before it. Do not whisper this, however, to others. There is One above who worketh in all things, and who governs even in the midst of that misrule to which the tendencies and powers of men are so easily perverted."

After which outburst he leaps, in the very next sentence, with a sigh of relief almost audible to us, to the much more congenial subject of oxygen and ozone. His letter to the *Times* of June 30, 1853, and his contribution to the *Athenæum*, are too long to quote here ; but he appears to have been exasperated by the attribution of the " results " claimed in table-turning to his pet forces of electricity and magnetism. There were many correspondents, strangers to him who expressed themselves quite frankly ; a surgeon in the Royal Navy, for one, wrote telling him that he had " missed his footing " in this particular matter. James Braid, however, supported him strongly. In a letter from Manchester he said : " It is no small gratification to me to have had my views of the nature and cause of Table-Turning confirmed and so ably ellucidated (*sic*) by your ingenious and conclusive physical tests." The subject cropped up a couple of years later when a Mr. Cox of Jermyn Street wrote to Faraday inviting him to witness the demonstrations of Home, the famous medium, " to show tables and chairs moving, and other phenomena much more extraordinary, without any person being near " ; only to receive for answer the following curt note :

" Mr. Faraday is much obliged to Mr. Cox, but he will not trouble him. Mr. Faraday has lost too much time about such matters already."

On this sheet Mr. Cox scrawled : " Sir,— You are wrong in not seeing me—*I have facts* which are at your service *now*—after to-day they will belong to others," and apparently sent it back to Faraday, since it is preserved among the documents at the Institution of Electrical Engineers.

Still later, having been again invited to be present at one of Home's séances, this time by Sir Emerson Tennant, he replied : " I do not wish to give offence to anyone, or to meddle with this subject again. I lost much time about it formerly in the hope of developing some new force or power ; but found nothing worthy of attention." And he goes on :

" I can only look at it now as a natural philosopher ; and because of the respect due to myself I will not enter upon any further attention or investigation unless those who profess to have a hold upon the effects agree to aid to the uttermost. To this purpose they must consent (and desire) to be as critical upon the matter, and full of test-investigation in regard to the subject, as any natural philosopher is in respect of the germs of his discoveries."

Towards the end of his life other suggestions of this kind reached him. One of these, a printed handbill with blanks for name, date, and hour, I have copied, as it came from the celebrated Davenport brothers in 1864 :

The Honor of
Dr. Faraday's

_____

Company is requested at a Private Séance to be given by the Brothers DAVENPORT and Mr. FAY, with the object of permitting certain so-called " Manifestations " to be tested by two Professors of Legerdemain, who have asserted their ability to expose an alleged fraud, and have been invited to attend the *Seance* for that purpose.

The *Seance* will be held at 326, Regent Street, on *Tuesday* 11*th* of October, at 3 o'clock precisely, in the presence of a select number of eminent Scientific and Literary Gentlemen.

An early reply would be esteemed a favour.

In handwriting at the bottom of this handbill are the words : " Mr. Boucicault had kindly granted the use of his house 326 Regent Street for the Séance—where replies may be addressed."

Faraday's answer to this was neat and sarcastic, with a genial touch :

" I am obliged by your courteous invitation, but really I have been so disappointed by the manifestations to which my notice has at different times been called, that I am not encouraged to give any more attention to them, and therefore I leave these to which you refer in the hands of the professors of legerdemain. If spirit communications not utterly worthless, of any worthy character, should happen to start into activity, I will leave the spirits to find out for themselves how they can move my attention. I am tired of them."

One more letter on the same subject, in response to a note from a stranger, is worth reading. Faraday was getting really angry with people who plagued him about " spirits."

" Sir,—I beg to acknowledge your letter of the 3rd, but I am weary of the spirits— all hope of any useful result from investigation is gone ; but as some persons still believe in them, and I continually receive letters, I must bring these communications to a close. Whenever the spirits can counteract gravity or originate motion, or supply

an action due to natural physical force, or
counteract any such action ; whenever they
can punch or prick me, or affect my sense
of feeling or any other sense, or in any other
way act on me without my waiting on them ;
or working in the light can show me a hand,
either writing or not, or in any way make
themselves visibly manifest to me ; whenever
these things are done or anything which a
conjuror cannot do better ; or, rising to
higher proofs, whenever the spirits describe
their own nature, and like honest spirits
say what they can do ; whenever by such-
like signs they come to me, and ask my
attention to them, I will give it. But until
some of these things be done, I have no more
time to spare for them or their believers, or
for correspondence about them."

It is impossible to avoid the thought that
in the prevailing humility and modesty of
his life there lurked a grain of intolerance ;
and it would be strange if it were not so,
however modified by charity and patience
was his Calvinistic upbringing. Very
rarely, however, does this mild resentment
appear in any phrase of his letters. With
honours conferred upon him by almost
every learned body of Europe and America

he had reason enough for pride, self-confidence, condescension ; yet the smallest tribute drew from him gratified appreciation, and he numbered himself with the least of those who serve science. " His standard of duty," says his biographer, " was supernatural. It was not founded upon any intuitive ideas of right and wrong ; nor was it fashioned upon any outward expediencies of time and place " ; it was formed entirely upon his religious faith, and it influenced almost every action of his life. " Any act of injustice or meanness called forth an almost volcanic burst of indignation," writes Professor Thompson. " Hot flashes of temper, fierce moments of wrath, were by no means unknown. But he exercised admirable self-control, and a habitual discipline of soul that kept his temper under." Similar evidence is given by his friend and successor Tyndall, who, almost to our astonishment, calls him " a man of excitable and fiery temper." But through self-discipline " he had converted the fire into a central glow and motive power of life, instead of permitting it to waste itself in useless passion." He never thrust his religious views on other people. " Never once," says the same friend, " during an intimacy of fifteen years, did he mention religion to me, save when I drew him on the subject." In our modern reactions from the *Little Henry and His Bearer* type of morals, we often too freely associate virtue with dull-ness and vice with brilliance ; but Faraday changed the terms of the equation and com-bined the brilliant and the good. And the only surd, the only unresolvable quantity, in his life was his frank and definite admission that for him personal religion and science were in separate compartments. But " *le cœur a ses raisons*," said Pascal, " *que la raison ne connait pas*," and the great debate goes on to-day and will go on while humanity gropes its way upward. " Objective evidence and certitude are doubtless very fine ideals to play with," wrote Professor William James, " but where on this moonlit and dream-visited planet are they to be found ? " [1] The thing is not to lose the dream in the multitude of business. " What ! " ques-tioned Blake of himself, " when the sun rises

[1] " The Will to Believe."

do you not see a round disc of fire, somewhat
like a guinea ? Oh, no, no ! I see an
innumerable company of the heavenly host,
crying, ' Holy, holy, holy, is the Lord God
Almighty ! ' " And again :

" How do you know but every bird that cuts
    the airy way
  Is an immense world of delight, clos'd by
    your senses five ? "

This is the vision which Faraday never lost,
however much he might analyse the sunrise
in terms of refraction and reflection. We
are not obliged to lose the thrill of music
when we study the nodes and harmonics of a
vibrating violin-string or the behaviour of a
column of air in an organ-pipe. Exploring
and desiring ever more definite evidence in
the physical world, Faraday was keenly alive
to the beauty of nature, and saw beyond it
another world in which his heart could believe, untroubled by speculation. His heart
had its reasons, and in him a deep-seated
faith and a magnificent intellect went in
harness together contentedly to the very end.

CHAPTER XI

The Closing Years

THE letter in which Faraday offered his resignation to those in control of the Institution that had been, in every sense, his home and incessant concern for nearly half a century must be given as it stands in Dr. Bence Jones' pages ; it is not one to spoil by an extract or a summary. It was sent in October, 1861 :

" It is with the deepest feeling that I address you. I entered the Royal Institution in March, 1813, nearly forty-nine years ago, and, with the exception of a comparatively short period, during which I was abroad on the Continent with Sir H. Davy, have been with you ever since. During that time I have been most happy in your kindness, and in the fostering care which the Royal Institution has bestowed upon me. Thank God, first, for all his gifts. I have next to thank you and your predecessors for the unswerving encouragement and support which you have given me during that period.

My life has been a happy one, and all I desired. During its progress I have tried to make a fitting return for it to the Royal Institution, and through it to science. But the progress of years (now amounting in number to threescore and ten) having brought forth first the period of development, and then that of maturity, have ultimately produced for me that of gentle decay. This has taken place in such a manner as to make the evening of life a blessing ; for whilst increasing physical weakness occurs, a full share of health free from pain is granted with it ; and whilst memory and certain other faculties of the mind diminish, my good spirits and cheerfulness do not diminish with them.

" Still I am not able to do as I have done. I am not competent to perform, as I wish, the delightful duty of teaching in the Theatre of the Royal Institution, and I now ask you (in consideration for me) to accept my resignation of the Juvenile Lectures. Being unwilling to give up what has always been so kindly received and so pleasant to myself, I have tried the faculties essential for their delivery, and I know that I ought to retreat ; for the attempt to realise (in those trials) the necessary points, brings with it weariness, giddiness, fear of failure, and the full conviction that it is time to retire ; I desire therefore to lay down this duty. I may truly say that such has been the pleasure of the occupation to me, that my regret must be greater than yours need or can be.

"And this reminds me that I ought to place in your hands the whole of my occupation. It is no doubt true that the Juvenile Lectures, not being included in my engagement as professor, were, when delivered by me, undertaken as an extra duty, and remunerated by an extra payment. The duty of research, superintendence of the house, and of other services, still remains ; but I may well believe that the natural change which incapacitates me from lecturing, may also make me unfit for some of these. In such respects, however, I will leave you to judge, and to say whether it is your wish that I should still remain as part of the Royal Institution. I am, Gentlemen, with all my heart, your faithful and devoted servant,

"M. FARADAY."

The Board of managers, to their honour, desired him to remain with the Institution, and he continued to take as active a part as his declining powers permitted ; but his last experimental research, on the effect of a powerful electro-magnet upon the spectrum of various chemicals, was carried out in the following year, and in that year, on June 20, he gave his last Friday lecture, on gas furnaces. Yet, as we have seen, he was still busy at lighthouse inspection, and some of his journeys at that age, and in days when rapid and comfortable transport was hardly known, must have tried his small reserve of strength severely—a trip to Dungeness, for example, in February, when he slept at the lighthouse, and went to sea at night in order to compare the visibility of oil lamp and electric light, and to test the effect of reflectors, at a distance of several miles.

Extraordinary, indeed, was his energy. " My words totter, my memory totters, and now my legs have taken to tottering," he writes to a friend in 1863, and then in 1864 he made twelve reports to Trinity House, some of them on complicated matters such as estimates and chemical analysis. His second letter of resignation to the Royal Institution, expressing his wish to retire from the position of superintendent of the house and laboratories, was dated March 1,

1865. He felt, he says, a growing inability to advise on matters of policy, and a reluctance to bear the responsibility of giving decisions upon questions of management ; he offers, if necessary, to vacate his rooms at the Institution—" for the good of the Institution is my chief desire in the whole of this action." Again the reply does honour to the managers. At their next meeting it was resolved unanimously :

" That the managers thank Professor Faraday for the scrupulous anxiety which he has now and ever shown to act in every respect for the good of the Royal Institution. They are most unwilling that he should feel that the cares of the Laboratories and the house weigh heavily upon him. They beg that he will undertake only so much of the care of the house as may be agreeable to him ; and that whilst relinquishing the duties of director of the Laboratory, he will retain his home at the Royal Institution."

To Dr. Bence Jones, who was then Secretary to the Institution, Faraday wrote expressing his affectionate thanks for this resolution.

He was now waiting for the end, watching

himself fade, and the picture of the old professor, perfectly aware of his weakness of
mind and body, calm in spirit, unshaken in
faith, neither longing for death nor fearing
it, is one which has more than a touch of
beauty. It is unspoiled by pain ; undis-
turbed by that heartache of the aged, the
feeling that they are not wanted. Occasionally his mind would wander for a while,
but not for long ; the subjects which had
constituted his lifework still had the power
to rouse him. In the winter of 1866, when
very feeble, he took the greatest interest in a
description of an electrical machine, sent to
him by a friend, and the sight of a long spark
from a new and powerful apparatus gave
him, almost at the last, perceptible pleasure.

Dr. Bence Jones called on him early in
August, 1867, at the summer home at
Hampton Court, and it was clear that he
could not last much longer. Day by day he
became weaker. His niece, Miss Jane
Barnard, who for several years had lived with
him and his wife almost as a daughter,
watched over him with unfailing devotion.
In one of her letters we have a picture of

these last months of the great philosopher: referring to Dr. Bence Jones, she says :—

" I then told him how in the course of the week, after my uncle had repeated the first verse of the 46 Psalm he turned to me and said " Who is Dr. Bence Jones' refuge and strength ? " The Dr. seemed quite touched. My Uncle has spoken oftener of him than of any one. . . . It was on Friday, 22 June that the attack of mental excitement came on ; I slept in the room two nights. . . . On Sunday . . . in the afternoon Dr. B. Jones came, but uncle hardly recognised him—he was in a heavy lethargic state, I suppose from the morphia he had at nights. Since then he has been gradually improving and now he is touchingly patient, quiet and happy, like a little child, so trusting. . . ."

" My last sight of him," said Mr. D. J. Blaikley, addressing the Institution of Electrical Engineers in 1915, " was about four months before his death, the time being April, 1867. At that time he had much failed, and his manner was that of second childhood. He was glad to be wheeled in a chair along the corridor and through his suite of rooms, and he sat at the window in the evening, as the light was failing, merely interested in watching the people going into the evening service in the chapel or church opposite."

At the last he took little notice of those round him, and he died on August 25, 1867, in his study chair. The funeral took place on the 30th, at Highgate, being, in accordance to his written and spoken wishes, very plain and private.

CHAPTER XII

Conclusion

FEW scientists have been so completely engrossed in their work through so long a period as was Michael Faraday ; yet we must not turn away from him under the impression that he was dull or uncompanionable. If he had no particular hobby or recreation, he joined in any fun that was going on, and all who knew him speak of the peculiar " brightness " and vivacity of his manner. He is described as being below the middle size, well set, active, and with extraordinary animation of countenance ; his pleasant laugh, his frankness, attracted all. " In his joyous enthusiasm," wrote Lady Pollock,[1] " he appeared like an inspired child. Quick feelings, quick movements, quick thought, vividness of expression and of perception, belonged to him. He came across you like a flash of light, and he seemed to leave some of his light with you. His presence was

[1] *St Paul's Magazine*, June, 1870.

always stimulating." Another writer re-members him as "hilariously boyish," and as never more at home, never so pleased, as when addressing an audience of children at Christmas and becoming a child with them. His course of six lectures on "The Chemical History of a Candle," delivered at the Royal Institution in the Christmas holidays of 1860–61, was printed in the *Chemical News* early in 1861 from shorthand notes taken by Mr. W. Crookes (Sir William Crookes, F.R.S.). They appeared in book form in the same year, and several editions have followed. These lectures show his love for children. "I claim the privilege of speaking to juveniles as a juvenile myself. . . . And now, my boys and girls," he begins.

He enjoyed boating, camping up the river, the Zoological Gardens—he was one of the earliest members of the Zoological Society, and his niece, Miss Reid, says, "We have seen him laugh till the tears ran down his cheeks as he watched the monkeys." Punch and Judy shows, acrobatic displays, and, above all, travelling, appealed to him. He was at heart a boy, despite the formality

of many of his youthful epistles—part of
which, no doubt, may be ascribed to the
customary precision of that period of "prunes
and prisms." After carrying out an ever-
famous experiment in 1821, with George
Barnard, and seeing for the first time a wire
charged with electricity revolve round the
pole of a magnet, he danced round the table,
his eyes shining, exclaiming, " There they
go ! There they go ! We have succeeded at
last ! " And he immediately proposed that
they should " celebrate " by spending the
evening at a theatre ; so off the two went to
Astley's.

Money did not appeal to him in the
slightest degree, save as a means to live in
moderate comfort. Many opportunities of
increasing his very slight income presented
themselves as his name began to carry
weight—requests to give expert evidence in
law cases, for example, when disputes turned
on scientific matters ; but one idea, as ever,
dominated his mind. " He might easily
have made £5,000 a year," says Tyndall,
" had he chosen to cultivate the professional
connection thus formed." Later on, when

his income from various sources averaged about £1,000 (it never exceeded £400 from his professorship), his domestic expenditure does not seem to have overstepped about half that figure, but there is no reason to suppose that he saved much ; he was too generous for money to stay in his pocket. It is said that he paid the expenses of boarding school for his young sister, and to do so went without dinner every other day. Professor Silvanus Thompson estimates that his gifts to the poor and sick amounted to several hundred pounds a year ; and he not only gave this practical help, but visited personally whenever possible. In a letter declining the suggestion that he should publish his lectures on metals, he said : " I have always loved science more than money, and because my occupation is almost entirely personal, I cannot afford to get rich." His professional income fell from £1,090 4s. in 1831 to £155 9s. in 1832—simply because science was his passion and the laboratory his real " place of business," his home, the central point of his thoughts. Professor Schonbein of Basle once worked for a whole day in that laboratory with Faraday ; one of the most enjoyable days, he records, that he ever spent in London. " After breakfast," he wrote, " I was supplied with one of the laboratory dresses of my friend, which, when I was presented in it to the ladies, gave occasion to no little amusement, as the dimensions of Faraday are different from those of *my* precious body ! "

Nothing causes more surprise, as we read Faraday's letters, than his complete indifference to politics, the great events, the international crises, of his day. People outside his immediate sphere of science are scarcely ever mentioned. It was during his most active years, the period covered between 1820, let us say, and 1860, that the railway became established ; the death of Huskisson through an accident at the opening of the Liverpool and Manchester line occurred in 1830. Hardly a reference to the new method of locomotion occurs in Faraday's correspondence, though we reasonably feel that such a man should have looked upon the arrival of steam transport and the growing speed of travel with lively interest. Trafalgar

Waterloo, Navarino, the Afghan War,
Sebastopol and Inkerman ; the Reform Bill
Riots, when the police were stoned and the
windows of Ashley House were smashed by
the mob ; the abolition of slavery ; O'Con-
nell and Ireland ; the repeal of the Corn
Laws ; the Cobbett trial ; the opening of
new London Bridge ; the coronation of
William IV., and the accession of Queen
Victoria ; the rise of Gladstone and Disraeli,
and the reverberant political duels of the
period ; Darwin's investigations and assump-
tions ; the growing fame of Lincoln in the
fifties ; the American Civil War of the
early sixties, the critical situation over the
Alabama and *Florida*—these find not even
an allusive place in such letters as have been
published. " The year 1843," says Morley
in his *Life of Cobden*, " was famous for a great
agitation in each of the three kingdoms " ;
yet no echoes of the strife are heard. Only
when some exalted personage actually inter-
sects Faraday's orbit, as with Lord Melbourne's offer of the pension, or the gift of
the house at Hampton Court by the Prince
Consort and the Queen, are we sure that he

was aware of another busy world outside his own. He was not like Sir Humphry Davy who " in the morning was the sage interpreter of nature's laws, and in the evening sparkled in the galaxy of fashion." " All philosopher and nothing of a quack," was the summary of *Punch*, in some verses which appeared in 1853 ; and *Punch* chaffed him for his guilelessness :

" Oh, Mr. Faraday, simple Mr. Faraday !
    Did you of enlightenment consider
      this an age ?
Bless your simplicity, deep in electricity,
    But in social matters, unsophisticated
      sage ! "

Nature, in all her aspects, he loved, and interpreted her laws also ; but he needed no relief of a " fashionable " kind—a quiet hour or two in his own rooms, with his own friends, provided him with rest. He would have been welcomed in any company ; William Thomson, writing in June, 1846, to his father, mentions that he attended one of Faraday's lectures, " which, though on his new discoveries, was very popular, and very interesting to a miscellaneous assemblage of fashionable people." The outside world, however, did not matter. Tremendous events were going on all round him, but to him the tremendous events were those occurring under the manipulation of his clever fingers, the conclusions drawn by his untiring brain. This exclusiveness bore no relation whatever to selfishness ; it was simply that here lay his road, and he had to follow it ; with the result that he is recognised as the prince of natural philosophy in his age, and as one with scarcely any rival even in later years.[1]

A letter was once addressed to him by a colleague abroad, " To Professor Michael Faraday, Member of all the Academies of Science, London " ; it gives a good idea of the repute in which other *savants* held him. He was asked by Henry Cole, C.B., of the Council on Education, to become a Vice-President of the Albert Hall, but

[1] At a demonstration of electro-magnetic rotation which took place during the recent Exhibition at King's College, London, some pretty experiments were shown. " We must go back to Faraday for the explanation," said the lecturer.

pleaded ill-health in his gentle refusal. " Remember," he wrote, " that I was obliged to decline lecturing before Her Majesty and the Royal Family at Osborne."

Those who knew him personally loved him ; he possessed in overflowing measure that quality which we can only describe as " charm." " He would peep into the laboratory when he thought me weary," says Tyndall, " and take me upstairs with him to rest." He never forgot the old times when he was a poor workman. As he left the Institution one evening with Tyndall, about 1856, to pay a visit in Baker Street, he took his friend's arm at the door and said : " Come, Tyndall, I will show you something that will interest you." This was the old shop in Blandford Street, where Faraday pointed out a little room with a window facing the road. " Look, Tyndall," he said ; " that was my working-place. I bound books in that little nook." Like many another who has left a trade learned in youth, he retained both skill in it and affection for it ; from time to time throughout his life he would bind a book simply for recreation, and it has not been my least pleasure, in preparing these pages, to handle some of his bindings and to observe their perfection.

Perhaps one of the finest tributes to him came from Sir William Thomson, afterwards Lord Kelvin. Presiding over the section of Mathematics and Physics at the British Association Meeting of 1867 at Dundee, he said in his opening address :

" It was my intention not to detain you from the interesting subjects and abundant matter for discussion which will so fully occupy our time during the meeting by an introductory address ; but I must ask you to bear with me if I modify somewhat this resolution, in consequence of a recent event which, I am sure, must touch very nearly the hearts of all present, and of very many in all parts of the world, to whom the name of Faraday has become a household word for all that is admirable in scientific genius. Having had so short a time for preparation, I shall not attempt at present any account of Faraday's discoveries and philosophy. But, indeed, it is very unnecessary that I should speak of what he has done for science. All that lives for us still, and parts of it we shall meet at every turn through our work in this section. I wish I could put in words something of the image which the name of Faraday always suggests to my mind. Kindliness and unselfishness of disposition ; clearness and singleness of purpose ; brevity, simplicity, and directness ; sympathy with his audience or his friend ; perfect natural tact and good taste ; thorough cultivation— all these he had to a rare degree ; and their influence pervaded his language and manner, whether in conversation or lecture. But all these combined made only a part of Faraday's charm. He had an indescribable quality of quickness and life. Something of the light of his genius irradiated his presence with a certain bright intelligence, and gave a singular charm to his manner which was felt by everyone, surely, from the deepest philosopher to the simplest child who ever had the privilege of seeing him in his home—the Royal Institution. That light is now gone from us. While thankful for having seen and felt it, we cannot but mourn our loss, and feel that whatever good things, whatever brightness, may yet be in store for us, *that* light we can never see again."

" In so perfect a character," says Professor Thompson, " it would be marvellous if there were not some flaw. His persistent ignoring of Sturgeon, and his attribution of the invention of the electromagnet to Moll and Henry, whose work was frankly based on Sturgeon's, is simply inexplicable. He failed to appreciate the greatness of Dalton, and thought him an overrated man." And Dr. Gladstone sounds a similar note when he observes of Faraday that, with his great caution and his repugnance to moral evil, he was more disposed to turn away in disgust from an erring companion than to endeavour to reclaim him.

His titles and honours increased in number year by year, and there is no need to recapitulate them here. He was a Fellow of many scientific Societies abroad, corresponding member of many more, Honorary Member of others ; received the Prussian Order of Merit ; was one of the eight Foreign Associates of the Academy of Sciences, Paris, and Commander of the Legion of Honour. Our English Universities, of course, asked his acceptance of their recognition of his scientific knowledge, and we have noted the unusual distinctions bestowed by the Royal Society. It is probably not so generally known, or is at least forgotten, that a deputation from the Royal Society waited upon him in 1857 to offer him the Presidency ; but he decided against this. The one-time errand boy received almost every honour which the whole world of science could give ; more than this, he was consulted by the Government on several occasions when expert advice was needed—the Home Office, Woods and Forests, Ordnance, and other departments applied to him, and he responded, declining payment, "as a good subject." He valued all these distinctions very highly, and when, in 1854, the Parliamentary Committee of the British Association asked his opinion upon the measures to be taken by the Government or the Legislature "to improve the position of science, or of the cultivators of science, in this country," he replied, in a dignified and graceful letter to Lord Wrottesley, the Chairman, that a Government should *for its own sake* honour the men who do honour and service to the country. Not by indiscriminate knighthoods and baronetcies, which "instead of conferring distinction confound the man who is one of twenty, or perhaps fifty, with hundreds of others," but by recognising the scientific men among its people as a class and exercising discretion in the bestowal of its careful favours.

The influence of Faraday's work upon other scientists cannot be expressed in set terms ; to gain some idea of its extent we may bear in mind that his name occurs in practically every text-book on electricity published to-day, and that an abbreviation of his name, the " farad," is used to denote the unit of electrical capacity—just as " volt," " ohm," and " amp " are derived from Volta, Ohm, and Ampère. His direct influence can sometimes be traced. Professor Silvanus Thompson, in his biography of Lord Kelvin (William Thomson) tells something of it. A cousin of Faraday, David Thomson, was Professor of Natural Philosophy at Glasgow University from 1842 to 1845 during the illness of Professor Meikleham, and afterwards held the Chair of National Philosophy at Aberdeen. By him William Thomson was " inoculated with Faraday fire." " Hitherto the doctrines taught him respecting electricity and magnetism had been on the then accepted lines of Newtonian forces acting at a distance. . . . David Thomson inculcated the Faraday conception of electric and magnetic forces acting along curved lines in the medium, and the further possibility of the screening of electric forces by the interposition of a conducting sheet. At first William Thomson rejected these notions, thinking them incompatible with first principles, and argued eagerly against Faraday's views. Ultimately he was convinced, and ever afterwards retained the most sincere admiration for Faraday and his work." Professor Clerk Maxwell, in the *Apologia* which he prefixed in 1873 to his *Treatise on Electricity and Magnetism*, wrote :

I found, also, that several of the most fertile methods of research discovered by the mathematicians could be expressed much better in terms of ideas derived from Faraday than in their original form. . . . If by anything I have here written I may assist any student in understanding Faraday's modes of thought and expression I shall regard it as the accomplishment of one of my principal aims : to communicate to others the same delight which I have found myself in reading Faraday's *Researches*.

The reader will begin to wonder whether Faraday's deductions were invariably right —whether he never made a false step. It is not absolutely true, says Dr. Gladstone, that the great scientist was never caught in a mistake ; but the extreme rarity of those mistakes, in spite of the immense amount of his published work, he characterises as " one of those marvels which can be appreciated only by those who are in the habit of describing what they have seen in the mysterious land that lies beyond the boundaries of previous knowledge." He visualised things. He saw, in his mind's eye, the lines of force passing through the air from the magnet, and precipitated the mist of speculation into the certainty that those lines did exist ; he even proved them to be definable and measurable. Oersted of Copenhagen, in 1819 or 1820, discovered the action of an electric current on a magnetic needle ; Ampère soon after showed that a conductor carrying current acts upon another similar conductor, and that all magnetic phenomena then known could be duplicated by the action of electric currents ; Faraday made history by proving that magnetism could produce or generate electric currents.

The great work which he began has been carried on and brought to an intensely interesting stage by many scientists, some whose names are familiar, others who are honoured more in scientific circles than by the public. Not a few of them laboured in Faraday's own lifetime. Joule, between 1840 and 1850, for instance, was carrying on some extraordinarily vivid researches into magnetism, heat, and energy only less valuable, perhaps, than Faraday's own work. William Thomson (afterwards Sir William Thomson, later on Lord Kelvin) in 1847 Professor of Natural Philosophy at Glasgow University, devoted many years to the study of magnetism. Sturgeon invented or devised the soft iron electro-magnet and studied its action deeply ; other names we have noted as occasion arose in this short survey ; and Clerk Maxwell, charming humorist and

Michael Faraday

superb mathematician, brought his magnificent skill to bear on the working out of theoretical problems arising from Faraday's conclusions which had been derived from practical experiments. To others, more than we can mention here, honour must be given. And, though the chief aspects of Faraday's ceaseless labours have been recorded here, there remain still a great many notable pieces of scientific investigation which must be left for the complete biography yet unwritten.

The first practical application of this science, which we must regard as the result of the combined labours of Volta, Ampère, Oersted, Arago, Ohm, Faraday, and others of the period, was the electric telegraph. In 1837 the telegraph of Cooke and Wheatstone in England was at work, and in 1840 that of Morse in America ; the story of the growth of submarine telegraphy is a fascinating one, and has been ably told in Lord Kelvin's life by Professor S. P. Thompson.

Since then the bounds of electrical knowledge and its application have been steadily extending. Upon the future course of the stream of electrical science, one of whose principal tributaries we have been following, it would be rash to say more than a word or two. When a cough in Pittsburg can be "heard" in telephones by British firesides within a time-limit of a fraction of a second, it seems less difficult to believe in miracles, and dangerous to say that anything is "impossible." In electrical matters we can be sure that Faraday's influence will never be lost, however many great discoveries may intervene ; his secure position as pioneer none can ever dispute.

PRINCIPAL DATES

1790   Benjamin Franklin died.

1791   Sept. 22.   Michael Faraday born.

1792   Shelley.   English poet, born.

1793   England and France at War.

1805   Battle of Trafalgar.

"   Faraday apprenticed to Bookbinding.

1809   Gladstone born.

1812   Napoleon entered Moscow.

"   Faraday attends lectures by Sir Humphry Davy at the Royal Institution.

1813   Faraday appointed Laboratory Assistant at the Royal Institution.

1813–15 Faraday's tour on the Continent with Sir Humphry Davy.

1814   Allied forces entered Paris.

1815   Battle of Waterloo.

1816   Faraday's first published paper in the *Quarterly Journal of Science*.

1819   Queen Victoria born.

1821   Faraday married to Miss Sarah Barnard. First paper read before the Royal Society.

PRINCIPAL DATES

1824 Faraday elected F.R.S.

1825 Faraday appointed Director of the Laboratory. Stockton and Darlington steam railway opened.

1827 Volta died. Battle of Navarino.

1831 Faraday succeeded in producing electricity from magnetism.

1835 Receives pension from Government in honour of his work.

1836 Becomes adviser to Trinity House.

1837 Queen Victoria ascended the Throne.

1839 Penny Postage introduced.

1848 Chartist Agitation.

1854 Crimean War.

1857 Indian Mutiny.

1861 Abraham Lincoln elected President of the United States.

1865 Faraday resigns from the Royal Institution.

"   Gladstone becomes Leader of the House of Commons.

1867 Faraday died, August 25th.

1868 Disraeli's first Ministry.

BOOKS RECOMMENDED

The Life and Letters of Faraday, by Dr. Bence Jones (2 Vols.)

Michael Faraday by J. H. Gladstone, Ph.,D., F.R.S.

Faraday as a Discoverer, by John Tyndall

The Life and Discoveries of Michael Faraday by J. A. Crowther, Sc.D.

Index

Index